CAPTAIN GRANT MARSH

OTHER BOOKS BY KEVIN KREMER:

A Kremer Christmas Miracle

Spaceship Over North Dakota

Saved by Custer's Ghost

The Blizzard of the Millennium

When it Snows in Sarasota

Santa's Our Substitute Teacher

Are You Smarter Than a Flying Gator

Maggie's Christmas Miracle

The Year Our Teacher Won the Super Bowl

The Most Amazing Halloween Ever

Are You Smarter Than a Flying Teddy

Angel of the Prairie

The Worst Day of School EVER—Do-Over

Valentine Shmellentine

CAPTAIN GRANT MARSH

The Greatest Steamboatman in History

by Kevin Kremer

Published by Kremer Publishing
2019
P.O. Box 1385
Osprey, FL 34229-1385

www.KevinKremerBooks.com

This book is dedicated to the great people of Mandan and Bismarck—and the rest of North Dakota. What a great place to grow up, work, and write about!

Also, to my former students—I never would have written any books without your encouragement. You've also become my favorite characters.

Also, to family and friends. There are no words—but AMAZING is a pretty good start.

Special Thanks

Extra special thanks to super-friend Dr. Duane Roth for doing a zillion book-building tasks during the three years I was working on this book.

Special thanks to Mikiel and Odell Ottmar for all their help.

Special thanks to artist Darrel Aleson for putting up with my demands and banter—and exceeding my expectations.

Dr. Duane Roth, the guy wearing the Northern Pacific Railroad hat with his hand on the hamburger platter at Ohm's in Mandan; Darrel Aleson, the bearded artist sitting next to him; Mikiel Ottmar, the lady with the big smile; Odell Ottmar, the husband sitting next to Mikiel

To Elisabeth Arena for her great work designing the book.

To nephew Will Volk for his excellent work on the book video.

To author Paulette Bullinger (author of Nothing Hidden) for her support—and the photo she took for me for this book.

To super-teacher Karen Smink for buying more of my books than any other teacher in the world during my 24 years of writing books.

To Michelle Long at the Rochester Area Historical Society in Rochester, Pennsylvania, for all her help.

To the Beaver County Historical Research and Landmarks Association in Pennsylvania for their help.

To all the great people at the Overholser Historical Research Center in Fort Benton, Montana, especially author Ken Robison.

To Carol Long for the look inside the Grant Marsh home in Yankton, South Dakota.

To Kremer Publishing's outstanding, underpaid IT (Information Technology) Department, and its leader, Ronald R. Ladd, for all their help with this book project.

To Mom and Santa—just because!

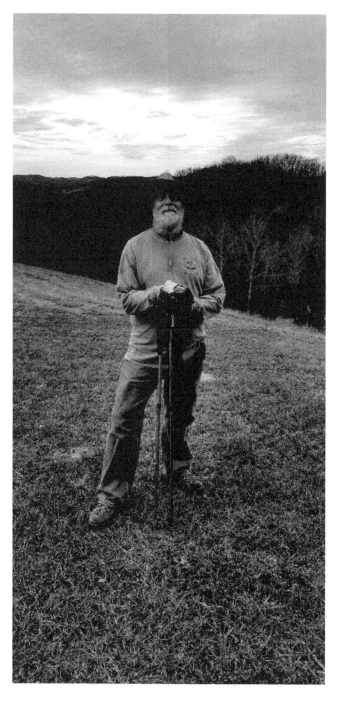

IT Leader and fruitcake connoisseur, Ronald R. Ladd

CONTENTS

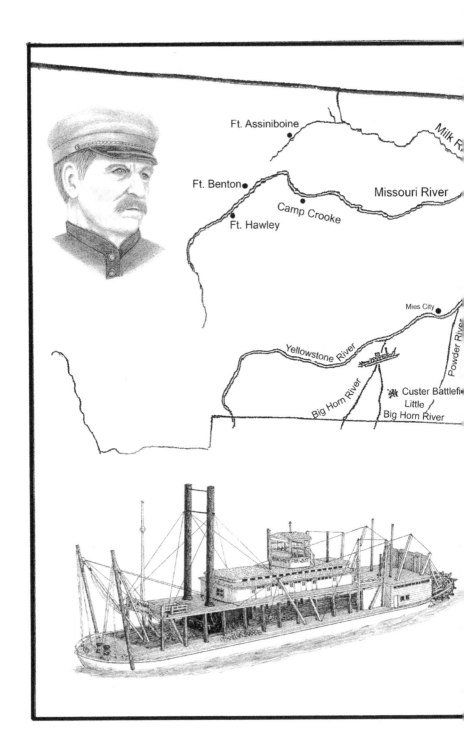

Ft. Assiniboine

Milk R.

Ft. Benton

Ft. Hawley

Camp Crooke

Missouri River

Mies City

Yellowstone River

Powder River

Big Horn River

Custer Battlefi

Little
Big Horn River

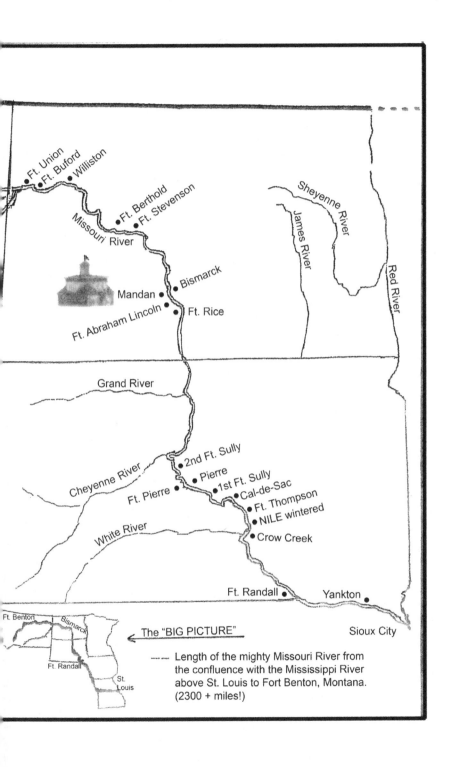

Ft. Union
Ft. Buford
Williston
Ft. Berthold
Ft. Stevenson
Missouri River
Sheyenne River
James River
Red River
Bismarck
Mandan
Ft. Abraham Lincoln
Ft. Rice
Grand River
2nd Ft. Sully
Pierre
Cheyenne River
1st Ft. Sully
Cal-de-Sac
Ft. Pierre
Ft. Thompson
NILE wintered
White River
Crow Creek
Ft. Randall
Yankton
Sioux City

Ft. Benton
Bismarck
Ft. Randall
St. Louis

The "BIG PICTURE"

- - - - Length of the mighty Missouri River from
the confluence with the Mississippi River
above St. Louis to Fort Benton, Montana.
(2300 + miles!)

CHAPTER 1

Catching Up with Sarabiskota

Unless you've been living on some deserted island completely shut off from the outside world, you already know about Prez and his nine good friends, including their amazing robot, Egore. They call themselves *Sarabiskota*, and they're recognized all over the world. Just in case you've forgotten their story, I'll refresh your memory a bit.

Going back four years, Egore was not in the picture yet. It was Prez and his eight friends—Jan Jones, Kari Wise, Katy Heidebrink, Jessie Angel, Chad Renner, Mike Schafer, Nick Hillman, and Kevin Feeney. All of these close friends, except Katy, had grown up in Bismarck, North Dakota. They had all just finished the seventh grade.

The kids are all precocious, but Prez brings new meaning to that word. His brain operates at a level that's almost unimaginable. He's constantly inventing new

1

things and exploring endless possibilities. At times, Prez can become a little scatterbrained when he's working on so many things at the same time, but his Sarabiskota friends help keep him as organized as possible.

You have to go way back to the second grade to find out how Prez, whose real name is Mike Gold, got his nickname. After he was done with a report on President Teddy Roosevelt that year, Mike told his teacher he wanted to be president of the United States someday, just like Teddy. After that, some of Mike's friends started calling him *Prez*, and the nickname stuck.

Anyway, four years ago, the summer after he completed the seventh grade, Prez and his parents moved from Bismarck to Sarasota, Florida. At the time, Prez's dad's software company won a big military contract from Central Command in Tampa, and Prez's dad relocated his business to beautiful Sarasota, a short distance to the south of Tampa Bay.

Although Prez had loved living in Bismarck his whole life, and he knew he would miss his friends from Bismarck a lot, the move to Sarasota was made much easier because Chad Renner's family moved there too. Chad's parents both worked for Prez's dad. In fact, their two families had been good friends for a long time.

Making things even better, Prez's and Chad's families found new beach homes on the same block on the north end of one of the most beautiful islands in the world, Siesta Key. There was only one house between Prez's and Chad's.

The boys were pleasantly surprised when they found out who lived in that house. It turned out to be a cute girl named Katy Heidebrink, who was the same age as the two boys. She had recently moved to Sarasota from Fergus Falls, Minnesota.

The two boys soon became friends with their neighbor girl, and they also gave Katy the nickname KT, which she really liked. KT's parents had bought a jet ski, bicycle, kayak, and parasailing business on Siesta Key called Siesta Key Water Fun.

Not long after Chad and Prez met KT, the three teens wanted to find out if it had ever snowed in Sarasota on Christmas, so they headed to the Selby Public Library in Sarasota to find out. While they were doing their research at the library, they stumbled upon a strange mystery involving a man known as Captain Sarasota who had disappeared from his fishing boat on Sarasota Bay a few years earlier. Captain Sarasota had left just one clue behind, a clue which no one had ever been able to figure out. It was a number carved into the steering wheel of his fishing boat—487699.

KT, Chad, and Prez immediately became obsessed with trying to solve this mystery. With the help of their other six friends back in Bismarck, who flew down to Sarasota to help them, they eventually solved the mystery, and it led them to a treasure worth hundreds of millions of dollars. You might have read about the whole thing in the book titled *When it Snows in Sarasota*.

Well, the teens became very wealthy, and during that time, Kari Wise came up with the name they still call themselves—*Sarabiskota*. The *Sara* part comes from *Sara*sota, the *bis* part comes from *Bis*marck, the *k* comes from North Da*k*ota and Bismar*ck*, and the *ota* comes from Saras*ota*, Minnes*ota*, and North Dak*ota*.

The past four years, the teens have been all over the

world, involved in more adventures, and they have become incredibly famous. A few years ago, Prez invented Egore, an advanced robot with a friendly, Frankenstein-like appearance, and Egore has become a super-important part of their group ever since.

One more thing—Sarabiskota has become *huge* Pittsburgh Steelers fans over the years. When given the opportunity two years ago, they decided to buy one-tenth of the team. They have also become big fans of the Philadelphia Eagles, largely because their favorite football player and friend, Carson Wentz, is such a terrific person and player, and he also grew up in their hometown of Bismarck.

You'll have no trouble remembering Egore and Prez, but just in case you still get the Sarabiskota teens mixed up, I'll remind you about each one of them, starting with the girls.

Jan Jones—Jan's friends call her Doc because she wants to be a medical doctor someday. She's been carrying a medical book around with her since she was a little girl. Doc's super-smart and very funny. She has long brown hair and wears glasses. Doc likes to play the clarinet, and her favorite sport is basketball.

Kari Wise—Kari's the tallest of the girls, and she's a natural leader. She keeps the group organized. She has short black hair and she likes to play soccer and ice skate.

Jessie Angel—Jessie's last name applies, or at least she has a guardian angel. You see, Jessie and her mom were riding in a car over a bridge near their home south of Bismarck when the bridge collapsed. Their car fell down into the river below, and they got out without even a scratch. It was a miracle! Jessie has very light blonde hair. She's artistic and really funny. She's also an excellent swimmer and likes to play the saxophone.

KT—Besides what you already know about KT, you might like to know that her favorite sports are volleyball and track. She's tall and has light blonde hair.

Chad Renner—Chad's a natural, all-around athlete. He's most talented at freestyle wrestling. Chad's tall with short black hair. He likes to play the trumpet, but doesn't seem to find much time to practice it.

Mike Schafer—Mike looks a lot like a young Elvis Presley and loves to sing and talk like Elvis. That's right. He's an Elvis impersonator, and he's really good at it. Besides that, Mike loves cross country running and playing his drums.

Nick Hillman—Nick asks tons of questions when he doesn't understand something. He loves to play hockey and football, and he's really good at both sports. Nick's a NASCAR fanatic and a huge University of North Dakota hockey fan. Nick is almost Chad's height with short brown hair.

Kevin Feeney—Kevin is the shortest of the group, and he's really strong. He has short, black, straight hair. Kevin is a talented quarterback, and he wants to keep growing and become as good as Carson Wentz someday.

CHAPTER 2

JB and Madison

"You've got to see this!" Madison called out as she focused on one of the seven huge monitors in front of her. "The front page of *The Bismarck Tribune* has a big photo of the Sarabiskota group along with a big story."

JB was about ten yards away from Madison in their spacious workshop. The two teens plus nine of their top technicians were focused on making some last-minute adjustments on the beautiful machine in front of them.

JB stopped for just a second and glanced over at Madison, her best friend and chief assistant. "Tell me about it," she said, quickly returning her major focus to the task at hand.

"Okay," Madison replied. "There's a photo of all of them, including their weird Frankenstein robot. They're all standing in front of a huge object covered with a tarp. The caption says that whatever's underneath that tarp is Sarabiskota's float for tomorrow's big Independence Day

Parade in Mandan, and it's over 150 feet in length. They're keeping it a big secret until tomorrow morning."

"What does the article say?" JB asked.

Madison got a mischievous look on her face. "I'll do that if you can name all ten Sarabiskota in less than 20 seconds," she said.

"Too easy," JB said confidently. "You've been my friend long enough to know I usually have a mnemonic device for things like that."

"Go ahead," said Madison. "Impress me."

"To start with," said JB, "for the first three names, I just remember *No Coins Please*, the title of one of my favorite books when I was a little girl."

"That Gordon Korman book," Madison recalled. "It was one of my favorites, too."

"Yup," said JB. "The "N" at the beginning of *No* stands for Nick Hillman, the most inquisitive of the Sarabiskotans, the "C" at the beginning of *Coins* stands for Chad Renner, and the "P" at the beginning of *Please* stands for Prez, the genius."

Madison chuckled. "And Prez is *also* the guy you have the huge crush on … who is *exactly* as old as you are *to the day* … who also might be even smarter than *you* are," she added. "Okay, that's three down, seven to go."

JB continued, "For the last seven, I just remember *three K's, two J's, and the two E's*. The three K's stand for KT Heidebrink, Kari Wise, and Kevin Feeney. The two J's stand for Jessie Angel and Jan Jones, who they call Doc. The two E's stand for Egore, their robot, and Elvis, who's really Mike Schafer, the famous Elvis impersonator."

"Not bad," said Madison.

JB chuckled. "You need to sound a little more impressed." … "Now, tell me what's in the newspaper."

"The headline is in big, bold letters—**Sarabiskota Insists Veterans Help Them Lead the Biggest Mandan Parade Ever!** Then it says:

Mandan, North Dakota, knows how to celebrate Independence Day, and tomorrow's parade celebrating the 250th birthday of the United States promises to be the biggest and best ever. Six months ago, Sarabiskota was asked to lead this year's special parade and they immediately said *yes*, but they made one request. They asked if the area's veterans could be part of their parade entry. Mandan's parade committee loved the idea, and Sarabiskota has had a large crew working on their special float ever since. Sarabiskota's float will be unveiled tomorrow morning in the parade's staging area on East Main Street at 8:30 a.m., just two hours before the parade begins. We expect their float will be a highlight of one of the best parades anywhere on this very special Independence Day celebrating 250 years of this great country.

Madison stopped reading from the newspaper. "Then the article goes on, catching everyone up with some of the things Sarabiskota has been up to since they solved that history mystery in Florida and found that treasure worth all that money."

"We know all that," said JB. "What else?"

"The article concludes with the Sarabiskotans sharing some of the things they looked forward to the most coming back to Mandan and Bismarck and celebrating this special Independence Day—besides the big parade."

"What did Prez say?" asked JB.

"Your *future boyfriend* can't wait to run the 5-K tomorrow morning before the parade with everyone. Oh … and a couple of them also mention the great fireworks display by the river at night. … If they only knew how *special* it's *really* going to be!"

"It should be unforgettable," said JB, glancing at the machine she was working on. "I think they're going to get a surprise they'll *never* forget."

"Do you think we're going to get Sarabiskota's attention?" asked Madison.

"Oh, I think that's a sure thing," JB answered. "They love trying to solve a good mystery—and we're going to give them one that will be impossible to resist."

"This is going to be fun!" said Madison.

"More than fun," said JB. "Now, I think it's time for us to take off for North Dakota. Let's get everyone together. It's time to give Sarabiskota and the rest of the world a mystery with lots of history that they will *never* forget."

CHAPTER 3

The Run For Fun

It was 7:00 a.m. on July 4, 2026—the 250th birthday of the United States of America. A huge crowd of runners, walkers, and spectators had gathered on West Main Street in Mandan, North Dakota, right in front of Ohm's Cafe, home of the best hamburgers in the world. It was almost time for the Mandan Independence Day Run for Fun 5-K.

Parked behind a large red start-finish line was a flatbed truck. Standing on the flatbed truck, microphones in hand, were two of North Dakota's most recognized people: Cara Mund, the governor of North Dakota, who was also Miss America of 2018; and Carson Wentz, quarterback of the five-time Super Bowl Champion Philadelphia Eagles.

"Happy Independence Day!" Cara Mund called out enthusiastically.

A huge cheer followed.

"Happy 250th Birthday, America!" Carson Wentz shouted.

Another huge cheer erupted from the crowd.

When the cheering had stopped, Cara announced, "Carson and I feel so honored to be the official starters for this Independence Day Run for Fun 5-K on this special birthday of our great country!"

"Cara, can you believe the turnout we have this morning!?"

The crowd cheered and cheered.

"It's awesome!" Cara exclaimed. "The race organizers told me the number of people registered this year completely obliterates the previous record!"

Carson added, "I have a feeling some famous participants in this race, who also happen to be the grand marshals for today's big parade, have a lot to do with that."

Another huge cheer went up from the crowd.

"Yes, that would be Sarabiskota!" said Cara. "And they're here with us today. Sarabiskota! Please come up here and join Carson and me!"

The crowd went wild as Sarabiskota emerged from a red, white, and blue tent next to Ohm's. They slowly moved through the enthusiastic, cheering crowd, greeting and high-fiving many of the people as they walked. Then they climbed the steps and joined Cara and Carson on the flatbed truck.

"Happy Independence Day, everyone!" Mike yelled.

A huge cheer and a bunch of screams followed.

"Kari, let me start with you," said Cara. "I heard you're all planning to run this 5-K together this morning at a slow pace. I'm just wondering. If none of you held back and you all ran as fast as you could, who would win?"

"Egore," Kari answered without hesitation. "I think he could outrun a racecar if he wanted to." The crowd laughed and cheered, and Egore had a big smile on his face.

Jessie said, "But we promised each other we'd run this 5-K at a slow pace. That way, we should all be able to finish the race as a group, and some of our friends out there can run with us, too, if they'd like to."

Another huge cheer erupted from the crowd.

"Mike," Carson began, and big cheers and screams instantly went up from the crowd.

"Wow!" said Carson. "You've got lots of fans out there, Mike! Are you planning on doing any singing during the parade later today?"

There were more screams, mostly from many of Mike's female fans in the crowd.

"Thank you. Thank you very much," Mike answered in his best Elvis voice. "You'll have to watch the parade to find out, but let me just remind everyone, I will be singing at the gazebo in Dykshoorn Park near the Mandan Train Depot from 4:00 to 5:00 this afternoon."

"That's awesome!" Cara said. "I'll be there, and it sounds like lots of your other fans will be there, too."

"KT," said Carson, "I heard you Sarabiskota girls designed and donated the special T-shirts that all the participants in this race are receiving. I see many people are wearing them right now."

Everyone cheered.

KT said, "The guys even helped with the design a little, but we had a great time working on it. I'm glad you like them."

"They're beautiful," said Cara.

"Nick," Carson continued, "I've heard you've been in town all week. What were some of the things you've been doing?"

"Well," said Nick, "besides working on the float, we went to eat at many of our favorite places like the Big Boy and A&B Pizza and Ohm's … we went out to Ft. Abraham Lincoln a few times … and we've had a chance to go to the rodeo and out on the Missouri River too."

"Carson and I actually ran into you at A&B," said Cara. "There's no better pizza anywhere, is there?"

"That's for sure," said Nick.

"Prez?" Carson began.

The crowd cheered and cheered.

"We've seen that incredible new aircraft of yours out at the Bismarck Airport. What inspired you to come up with such a beautiful souped-up version of the spaceship *Enterprise* from the *Star Track* movies?"

"Well," said Prez, "you know how much I love our space program and the old *Star Track* series with the *Enterprise* and the shuttlecraft *Galileo*. It seemed like the perfect thing to do."

"And you guys named the large craft the *Exercise* and your shuttlecraft is called the *Flying Teddy*," said Carson.

"Yes, it was a group decision," said Prez. "We all like to exercise a lot, and you know how much Teddy Roosevelt means to me and everyone else in this state."

"That's for sure," said Carson. "Is it true the *Exercise* model toy is now the most popular toy in the world?"

"It is," said Prez, "but the Egore toy is just about as popular."

"Is that right, Egore?" Cara asked.

"I guess so," said Egore, blushing.

"We all love you, Egore," said Doc. "You're the best!"

The biggest cheer yet went up from the crowd.

Carson asked, "Kevin, do you think you would consider taking Cara and me with you for a ride on the *Exercise* and the *Flying Teddy*?"

"Anytime," said Kevin. "Just let us know."

"I can't wait!" said Cara.

"Chad, where are you watching fireworks tonight?" asked Carson.

"After the rodeo tonight, we'll be headed to Nick's parents' cabin on the Missouri River," answered Chad. "The fireworks displays out on the river are always fantastic, but this year they're supposed to be the best *ever*."

"Sounds great!" said Carson.

"Doc, what are you all doing right after this morning's race?" asked Cara.

"We're going to get some burgers from Ohm's … then we have our float unveiling to go to."

"Mike," said Carson, "we've heard you have a song to sing to us before we start this 5-K run."

There was lots of screaming and cheering.

"Thank you. Thank you very much," Mike said in his Elvis voice. "I'm so happy to be here with all of you this morning, running and having some fun together on this very special Independence Day. … I think all of you will recognize this tune from one of my greatest songs … it's called 'Suspicious Minds.' I've changed the lyrics a little in honor of this special occasion."

Mike began singing in his incredible Elvis voice:

We're running the 5-K,
Now, let's get going,
Because we love it too much baby.

Why can't you see,
You can run with me,
I won't leave you in the dust today.

Let's go and run together,
With Independence Day on our minds,
And it's our country's 250th birthday,
Happy Birthday U.S.A! Let's go running!

***

West of Mandan on old Highway 10, JB and Madison cheered as a large group of runners, which included Sarabiskota, ran slowly by them.

"Don't you wish we were running with them?" Madison asked her friend.

"Even at that pace, I don't think either of us could finish a 5-K," JB answered. "We need to work out more."

"That's for sure," said Madison. "Right now, though, let's beat the crowd to that Ohm's place and try one or two of those famous hamburgers."

CHAPTER 4

The Mandan Independence Day Parade

More than 500 parade entries lined up in their designated positions around the enormous Rodeo Grounds Complex on Memorial Highway in East Mandan. There were marching bands, flying vehicles, floats, huge balloons, horses, vintage automobiles, fire engines, trucks and tractors of all sizes, and a wide variety of other entries from all over the United States.

Amid that organized chaos, a huge crowd had gathered near Mandan's McDonald's to watch the unveiling of the float that would lead the parade— Sarabiskota's float. Suddenly, everyone looked up into the sky as two large red, white, and blue drones approached from the east. They flew low over the area south of Mandan's McDonald's where the gigantic float that would lead the parade was setting, covered by an enormous red, white, and blue tarp.

Standing near the float, looking up in the sky at the drones, were more than 200 United States Veterans who would be either riding on the float or marching behind it.

In the middle of them was Sarabiskota.

The drones hovered 50 feet above the float then slowly descended, hooking the large rings attached to the tarp. Then the tarp was slowly lifted, as the song "God Bless America" was sung by seven gigantic, lifelike figures standing on the float.

"Ahhhhh!" The crowd was amazed at what they were seeing! The seven lifelike figures in front of them each stood over 20 feet in the air—and they all looked so incredibly real!

Prez announced, "Sarabiskota is so honored to be leading this wonderful parade along with many veterans from the area on this super-special 250th birthday of the United States of America! When we designed this float, we wanted to also honor some of the great people who helped make North Dakota the awesome state that it is today. Now, it is my great pleasure to introduce my friend Teddy Roosevelt, who will introduce the other famous people on the float."

The gigantic Teddy Roosevelt smiled the biggest toothy smile. "Why, thank you, Prez! Howdy everyone! I'm President Teddy Roosevelt, but you can just call me *Teddy*. Before I introduce you to each of my friends here, starting with the beautiful ladies, I must tell you something most important. I never would have been president of this great country if it had not been for my experience here in North Dakota!"

The crowd cheered enthusiastically. They couldn't believe how real Teddy looked and sounded.

"I love North Dakota and everything this state did for me in my life! You've probably already heard the story about my wife and mother both dying on Valentine's

Day in 1884. It was an awful day! Just *awful*! After that, I came here to North Dakota and lived a vigorous life in the Badlands—a vigorous life I truly loved! The time I spent in North Dakota helped me become stronger in body and spirit, and it helped prepare me for many challenges I'd face the rest of my life, including being president of these great United States of America!"

Everyone cheered and cheered—and cheered some more!

"Now, enough about *me*!" Teddy said. "Let me introduce the rest of the people riding on this float with me this morning, beginning with the young lady to my right, Hazel Miner. Talk about a real hero! Hazel, what you did during the Blizzard of 1920 near Center, North Dakota, is one of my favorite stories of all-time! I think it should be made into a movie! It would be a *blockbuster*!"

The gigantic Hazel Miner smiled and then spoke. "Teddy, you're much too kind. It's hard to believe more than 100 years have passed since my younger brother and sister, Emmet and Myrdith, and I got lost in that awful March blizzard while trying to get home from school on our horse-drawn sleigh, and it definitely was a difficult ordeal. What I did that day to save my two siblings is just what any other sister would have done."

Teddy said, "Actually, Hazel, what you did during that blizzard is one of the most amazing things I've ever heard of! … We'll be talking to you more about it on the parade route, and we'll be singing the beautiful song "The Ballad of Hazel Miner" that I love so much. We love you, Hazel!"

Everyone cheered and cheered.

"Thanks, Teddy, and everyone else," Hazel Miner replied. "I love you all!"

The crowd cheered some more.

Teddy said, "Next, I want you to meet the beautiful Shoshone woman who helped the Lewis and Clark Expedition as it traveled thousands of miles between North Dakota and the Pacific Ocean. Sakakawea, I read someplace that you have more memorials built in your name and more landmarks named after you than any other woman in the history of this great country! Although we don't seem to agree on how your name is pronounced or spelled, everyone agrees that the Lewis and Clark Expedition would not have been successful without you. It was certainly one of the greatest adventures in *history*, and you were largely responsible for its success!"

Sakakawea smiled and said, "My friends Captain Lewis and William Clark had so much to do with our success, but I'm glad I could do my part for this great country! Happy 250th birthday to the United States of America!"

Everyone cheered.

"Next," said Teddy, "we get to meet a beautiful lady who has the voice of an angel—born in Jamestown, she is one of the most brilliant, popular music performers *ever* in our great country. Peggy Lee, you are my favorite singer of all time. Would you please sing a little for us now?"

"I'd be happy to," the Peggy Lee figure replied. "Before I do, though, I'd just like to thank you all for making me part of this amazing celebration today."

Everyone cheered. Then Peggy Lee sang the first portion of her big hit song "Fever." Her voice was awesome!

"Thank you so much!" Peggy Lee said when she was

finished, and then everyone cheered enthusiastically, then cheered some more.

"That was simply *the best*!" Teddy exclaimed. "Now, let's go to another famous performer who grew up near here in Strasburg, North Dakota—a *great* entertainer—Lawrence Welk!"

The crowd applauded as a huge Lawrence Welk figure holding a gigantic accordion spoke with his unique German accent. "Wunnerful! Wunnerful!" he began. "Millions of people all over this country watched my television show each week that featured my champagne music. Yes, I was born on a farm near Strasburg, North Dakota, and they say I became one of the greatest entertainers in the world. A one and a two and a ..."

Then Lawrence Welk started playing the song "Accordion Polka" on the giant-sized accordion he was holding. After about 20 seconds, he stopped and the crowd cheered.

Teddy said, "That's *wunnerful*—I mean *wonderful*, Lawrence. Now, let's say hi to a man who has done so much for me and my legacy in North Dakota."

"I'm Harold Schafer!" a large figure spoke with joy and enthusiasm. "I was born in the little town of Stanton, North Dakota, and I founded a company known as Gold Seal with products that became pretty famous worldwide, like Mr. Bubble, Snowy Bleach, and Glass Wax. I tried to use the money I made to help others and especially to bring Teddy's spirit alive by turning Medora, North Dakota, in Theodore Roosevelt National Park into a world-class tourist destination."

The crowd applauded vigorously. "You've certainly done all of that!" Teddy replied. "I love you, Harold!"

"I love you, too, Teddy!" replied Harold.

Teddy continued. "Now, George Custer, you're next. I know you had that unfortunate experience at the Little Big Horn in Montana, but your life was just amazing! People might know about you commanding Ft. Abraham Lincoln from 1873 until 1876, but I wonder if they know that you were a *great* Civil War hero!"

The giant Custer figure spoke. "Thanks, Teddy! Has everyone been down to Ft. Abraham Lincoln lately? It's just a few miles south of here. They've almost totally rebuilt it, and it looks better than ever. There are fewer mosquitoes than when I lived there—and the air-conditioned buildings are definitely a huge improvement, too."

Teddy said, "George, your house is one of the biggest attractions down there at Ft. Abraham Lincoln. That whole state park by the Missouri River is just beautiful!"

"I hope everyone will come and visit us," said George Custer, "but right now, do you think we should get the parade started?"

"YES!" everyone yelled back.

"Then, let's get going!" Teddy yelled. "Parade entrants—start your engines … or do whatever you need to do to get ready!"

***

And *what* a parade it was!

JB and Madison watched from a great vantage point across the street from Mandan's historic Northern Pacific Train Depot.

"Do you think our surprise tonight can top this parade?" JB asked Madison.

"It's going to be tough, but I think so," JB replied with a smile.

CHAPTER 5

Fireworks after the Fireworks

As the nine o'clock hour approached, Sarabiskota sat around a fire in the backyard of Nick's parents' cabin on the west bank of the Missouri River.

KT looked around the fire at the faces of her friends. "What a day!" she exclaimed.

"The best!" said Jessie. "My grandpa used to tell us grandchildren about the North Dakota Centennial Celebration in 1989 and how incredible it was, but I have a feeling this beats it."

"How could *anything* top this?" Chad added.

"What are you all going to remember the most?" asked Egore.

"The faces of all the happy people along the parade route," said Prez. "Everyone was having such a great time."

Kari chuckled, "How 'bout all those girls screaming at you guys?"

"We can't help it if we're irresistible." said Kevin, giggling. "But I noticed you girls had plenty of guys screaming and yelling out your names, too."

"Egore might have had the craziest fans of anyone," said Nick. "Everyone loves you, Egore."

"What can I say?" said Egore, smiling.

"It's been a great week," Doc said. "I'm going to miss being around here."

"No doubt," said Mike. "Tomorrow we have to leave here and go to Australia for that big technology conference."

***

The big fireworks displays began at about 9:30 all up and down the Missouri River—and what an extraordinary sight it was! Hundreds of boats of all sizes were loaded with passengers, all of them enjoying the incredible spectacle from the river. Thousands more watched from the riverbank.

At midnight the fireworks ended, and Sarabiskota, along with everyone else, got ready to go home. ... Then, they got a HUGE surprise!

Suddenly, what looked like an old steamboat, all lit up spectacularly in multi-colored lights, moved slowly down the Missouri River past them!

"What's that!?" Jessie exclaimed.

"It's beautiful!" said KT.

"Look!" Chad exclaimed. "The lights just changed. I think they're spelling out something."

"They say **Remember Grant Marsh!**" Doc said.

"I never heard of Grant Marsh," said Nick. "Where is that located?"

At that moment, Nick's dad came running up to them. "Let's get in my boat and follow!" he said to Sarabiskota.

They quickly got onboard the 40-foot pontoon named *Recess Time* and joined the huge procession of boats, all following the steamboat, all headed slowly down the Missouri River.

"Look!" exclaimed Kevin. "The boat says *Far West* on it! Anyone know anything about the *Far West* or *Grant Marsh*?"

Egore had the answer immediately. "This is quite incredible," he said. "It turns out something pretty amazing was happening right here on the Missouri River almost exactly 150 years ago on July 5, 1876, the day after the United States was celebrating its 100th birthday. It involved both a man named Grant Marsh and a steamboat called the *Far West*."

"What!?" said Kevin. "I can't believe I've never heard about that!"

"I agree," said Egore. "Just think, exactly 150 years ago tonight, a steamboat captain named Grant Marsh was guiding his steamboat named the *Far West* right along the river here, down to Ft. Abraham Lincoln south of Mandan. On board were wounded soldiers from the Battle of the Little Big Horn—the battle where Custer and all his men were killed. "

"No way!" said Prez.

CHAPTER 6

The Far West Story

"I don't see anyone on board the steamboat," said Jessie.

"Me neither," said Kevin. "This is amazing!"

"I wonder who's doing all of this," said Chad.

"And *why* ?" said Mike.

"We'll figure all that out later," said Prez. "Right now, Egore, could you do some quick research and tell us the story of the *Far West* that took place 150 years ago?"

"Are you sure?" asked Egore. "You don't want to be distracted from all of *this*, do you? This has got to be one of the most incredible things to ever happen on this river!"

"We can handle the distraction, Egore," said Doc. "Please tell us the story."

"Yeah," Nick added. "I love a good story, and you've become pretty good at telling them."

"Well, thanks," said Egore. "I'll do the best I can,

but this is all so phenomenal! Where do you want me to begin?"

"Maybe start by telling us a little bit about what it was like around here in 1876," KT suggested.

"Okay," said Egore, "please turn your phones on so I can send you some photos as I go along. ... Just imagine, the railroad had gotten as far as Bismarck three years before 1876, but it hadn't crossed the Missouri River yet, so there were no bridges here. There were some ferries, though, in case you wanted to cross the Missouri River that way. Bismarck had a population of around 2,000 and it was a really dangerous place to live back then—a real wild western town. Custer had been at Ft. Abraham Lincoln since 1873, and Mandan didn't really exist yet. With the large fort on the Mandan side of the river, though, it wouldn't be long before the town of Mandan would spring up."

THE BISMARCK BOAT LANDING IN 1876;
STATE HISTORICAL SOCIETY OF NORTH DAKOTA

BISMARCK MAIN STREET IN 1877, LOOKING WEST FROM THE
SHERIDAN HOUSE; *NORTH DAKOTA STATE UNIVERSITY ARCHIVES*

FT. ABRAHAM LINCOLN IN 1876; *STATE HISTORICAL SOCIETY OF
NORTH DAKOTA*

GEORGE ARMSTRONG CUSTER HOLDS A MUSICAL SCORE WHILE A WOMAN PLAYS THE PIANO AT THE CUSTER HOUSE IN 1876; *STATE HISTORICAL SOCIETY OF NORTH DAKOTA*

"Egore, please tell me there was an A&B Pizza place around back then," Nick said with a chuckle.

"Sorry, Nick," Egore replied, giggling, "your favorite pizza place didn't come to this area until 1969, about 93 years after this."

"I'm so glad I was born when I was," said Nick. "Life would be cruel without A&B Pizza."

"Just think," Egore continued, "it would actually be 13 years until North Dakota would even become a *state*. Yankton was the capital of the Dakota Territory in 1876, not Bismarck."

"Unreal," said KT.

"So," Egore continued, "Captain Grant Marsh and the *Far West* were working for General Sheridan of the U.S. Army that summer of 1876. Both the captain and his steamboat were an important part of a huge campaign being waged against a large group of Sioux Indians in Montana who resisted being forced to move to reservations. The *Far West* was serving several purposes for the Army in its campaign. It was being used as a supply ship, it ferried troops across the rivers when needed, it served as a command post for the officers, and it was a hospital ship."

"Where had the *Far West* come from?" asked Nick.

"The *Far West* had come from Yankton, South Dakota, on the Missouri River after the spring thaw. That's where Grant Marsh lived at the time. The *Far West* had actually stopped at Ft. Abraham Lincoln on May 27, and when they unloaded supplies at the fort before going on up the river, they found out that Custer and his men had already left on their march to Montana ten days earlier."

"Did Captain Grant Marsh know Custer?" asked Mike.

"He sure did," said Egore. "He knew Custer's wife, Libbie, too, plus a lot of the soldiers at the fort. When the *Far West* was unloading supplies at Ft. Abraham Lincoln on the 27th of May, Libbie and some other women from the fort came on board the *Far West* for lunch, and Libbie asked Captain Marsh to take her along up to Montana."

"What did Captain Marsh say?" asked Jessie.

"He didn't really want any extra passengers who were not critical to the military campaign. He convinced her to wait and take another, more comfortable steamboat that would be going that way later," Egore explained.

"Did she ever see her husband again?" Chad asked.

"It's so sad, but *no*," Egore replied. "It looks like the

Far West steamboat we're following right now is a beautiful model of the actual *Far West*. This one is about one-third the size of the one that came by here 150 years ago. The real *Far West* was 190 feet long and 33 feet wide. If you want to glance at your phones, here's what it looked like."

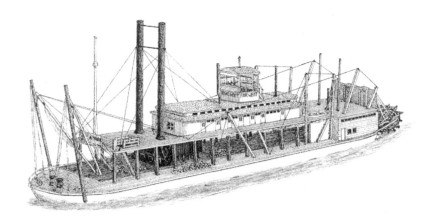

"This one probably has a few more lights than the real one, too" said Kevin.

"Definitely," said Egore. "The one in front of us is giving us an extraordinary light show. There were no electric lights like this back in 1876, mostly gas lights, kerosene lamps, and candles. Edison didn't even develop a decent light bulb until about 1880. ... Anyway, getting back to what was happening at this time 150 years ago, I'll send a map to each of your phones now so you can follow along with the story if you'd like. ...

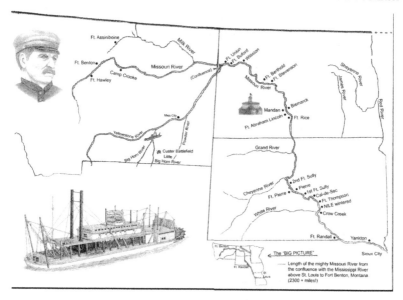

"All right ... by the time Custer's men were killed on June 25, Grant Marsh had actually positioned the *Far West* near the mouth of the Little Big Horn River, as close as possible to where the suspected battle would take place. The fact that Grant Marsh was able to get his boat to that position was a miracle in itself. No steamboat had ever traveled that far, and it was almost impossible to navigate something as large as the *Far West* on a river like that. The Big Horn River was narrow and shallow and filled with snags and islands and other obstacles, which made it almost impossible for a steamboat to maneuver. Also, steamboats like the *Far West* were easy targets for the Indians because the river was so narrow in many places. But somehow, Grant Marsh was able to do it."

"Did the *Far West* have any protection?" asked Kari.

"Yes, there were about 60 soldiers on board," Egore answered. "The pilot house, where Grant Marsh spent a lot of his time, was reinforced with iron, and there were sand bags in other places to stop the bullets.

41

"So," Egore continued, "the Battle of Little Big Horn takes place—sadly, Custer's men were all killed but there were numerous soldiers involved in the battle besides Custer's. There were many wounded men who needed to get to the good hospital at Ft. Abraham Lincoln south of Mandan—and that's where the heroic story involving Captain Grant Marsh and the *Far West* comes in."

"Were there any doctors on board?" asked Doc.

"Yes, there was one doctor on board the *Far West* named Dr. Williams and another who came on board with the wounded named Dr. Porter. Dr. Porter was actually one of three doctors who had been out on the battlefield during the fighting. He was also the only one who survived. He was a real hero, treating the injured before they got to the *Far West* and after they got on board too. Before the wounded arrived, Dr. Williams and the some of the men on board the *Far West* laid down a thick layer of fresh grass covered by canvas to make a good mattress for the wounded to lie on."

"How many wounded were there?" asked Doc.

"There were 52 wounded men and a wounded horse. They really needed to get to the hospital at Ft. Abraham Lincoln south of Mandan as fast as possible, but it was more than 700 miles away. Grant Marsh was really determined to get there as fast as he could—but he knew how dangerous the trip would be."

"There was a wounded *horse* on board?" asked KT.

"Yes, his name was Comanche. The soldier who had ridden Comanche was named Captain Keogh, and he was one of Custer's men. Comanche was severely wounded, but thankfully, there was a veterinarian with the troops who treated Comanche's wounds."

"Please tell me Comanche lived," KT pleaded.

"He did," said Egore. "In fact, he became quite famous. He lived another 14 years, and he was treated like a prince. After Comanche died, they even preserved him, and he's now on display in a museum at the University of Kansas."

"They *stuffed* Comanche?" Nick said, grimacing.

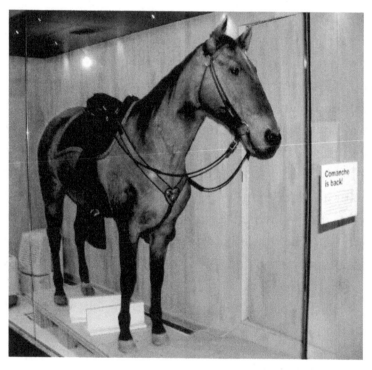

COMANCHE AT THE UNIVERSITY OF KANSAS; *LIBRARY OF CONGRESS*

Egore giggled. "I guess that's another way of putting it. ... So, the wounded were on the *Far West*, and they were ready to take off for Ft. Abraham Lincoln. Grant Marsh said it was so lucky that Dr. Porter had survived, because the wounded really needed someone like him.

He was a real hero—he tended to the wounded day and night, under some really tough conditions."

"Whatever happened to Dr. Porter?" asked Doc.

"Dr. Porter became a real leader in Bismarck and Mandan. He became a prominent doctor and investor. He was even a founder of the First National Bank of Bismarck and the State Bank of Morton County in Mandan.

"Now, back to the story. They've got over 700 miles to travel. The first 53 miles on the Big Horn River to the Yellowstone River were very treacherous, and Captain Marsh wondered if he could even do it. Having all those wounded men on board, traveling with the current on a river that was really hard to navigate—all this was weighing heavily on Captain Marsh. He thought he was probably going to smash the steamboat up trying to do it. But another man on board assured Captain Marsh he could do it—which gave the captain just the extra confidence he needed at this extremely challenging time, and soon they took off on that first part of the trip, down the Big Horn River.

"They do this during the daytime, but it was really rough going. Dr. Porter described it as a real rollercoaster ride, where sometimes they would hit something and they'd all fall down like bowling pins. Grant Marsh guided the *Far West*, as only he could, dodging rocks and snags and sandbars, while the *Far West* was being pushed by a strong current. It took all the skill of Captain Marsh and a lot of luck to get them to the Yellowstone River, but they made it.

"Once they got to the Yellowstone River, Grant Marsh wanted to immediately go on to Ft. Abraham

Lincoln from there, but they were delayed, having to ferry other troops across the river. By the time they left for Ft. Abraham Lincoln on July 3 at 5:00 p.m., there were 38 wounded on board. Fourteen of the wounded soldiers were now well enough to remain at a military camp that was located there. After that, they traveled the remaining 710 miles on the Yellowstone and Missouri Rivers day and night in record time, making it right to where we are at about 11:00 p.m. on July 5, 1876, and it took 54 hours. That was a record that would never be broken, and it was a record broken under awful conditions."

"Did you say they traveled at night!?" asked Nick.

"Yes, they didn't have headlights or anything, but they had some moonlight and what were called torch baskets. Those were nothing more than iron baskets, filled with burning fuel, lowered over the sides, so they would know where they were going in shallow water, and they could watch out for snags and stuff. Being that the steamboats were made mostly of wood, you can bet there were some fires over the years because of torch baskets. By the early twentieth century, there were electric lamps and lights on the steamboats."

"Did all the wounded make it back to Ft. Lincoln?" asked Doc.

"All but two," said Egore. "One, named Private William George, died and they stopped and buried him near the Powder River. Another was wounded, but he was well enough to be dropped off at Ft. Buford. They also stopped at Ft. Stevenson, nine miles southwest of where Garrison is now, where the *Far West's* flag was lowered to half-mast and her bow was draped in black in honor of the dead and wounded. … It's hard to imagine what it was like at 11:00 p.m. on July 5, 150 years ago, as the *Far West*, draped in black, approached the Bismarck steamboat landing, her whistle screaming."

"I can't imagine how everyone must have felt," said KT, sadly.

"Just awful," said Prez. "It makes me really sad just to think about it. But I'll bet Captain Marsh was relieved that they'd made it safely."

"Yes," said Egore. "One of the first men they woke up in Bismarck was the editor of the *The Bismarck Tribune* and the telegraph operator named J.M. Carnahan. For the next 22 hours, Carnahan barely moved from his chair, and he sent one of the longest telegrams ever, telling the story of what had happened at the Little Big Horn. There was a *Tribune* reporter named Mark Kellogg who had actually died with Custer's troops, and his notes leading up to the battle were included in the story. It turns out the telegram that Carnahan sent was one of the longest and most expensive telegrams ever, and Carnahan actually became quite famous for what he did. The telegram was more than 15,000 words long and cost about $3,000 to send, which is about $66,000 today."

"Really?!" Nick exclaimed.

"Yes," answered Egore. "And the newspaper story that was written was *huge* news at the time."

"What about Captain Marsh and the *Far West?*" asked Kari.

"Grant Marsh didn't stick around Bismarck very long," said Egore. "He wanted to get to Ft. Abraham Lincoln as soon as possible. Dr. Porter was relieved by some other doctors in Bismarck before the steamboat left for the fort."

Jessie said, "Those last few miles must have been so tough for Grant Marsh and everyone on the *Far West*."

"And when the people saw the *Far West* coming, draped in black … it must have just been *really* sad," Kevin added.

"It was," said Egore. "The officers at the fort got all the women to meet at the Custer House and then they got the bad news. Later, Libbie Custer sent a carriage to pick up Captain Marsh so she could talk to him, but he was feeling so awful about everything, he didn't meet with her."

"This is so sad, but you did a great job telling the whole story, Egore," said Kari, with tears running down her cheeks.

CHAPTER 7

Taiwan Scone

Many people on board the boats following the *Far West* took videos and photos with their phones and shared them with friends. Some posted them to Spacebook and other sites on the Internet. Soon, millions of people were watching the incredible spectacle taking place on the Missouri River south of Bismarck and Mandan.

The *Far West* slowly approached the shore near Ft. Abraham Lincoln. By this time, two helicopters flew over the scene.

"I can't believe this!" Doc exclaimed.

"What do you think is going to happen next?" Mike asked.

They didn't have long to find out. As everyone watched with great anticipation ... suddenly, rotor blades, totally lit up in red light, emerged from the top of the *Far West*. Then the steamboat lifted off the river, gained altitude to just under 50 feet, then slowly flew toward the fort. When it got to the Custer House, it hovered above it for more than three minutes as it flashed

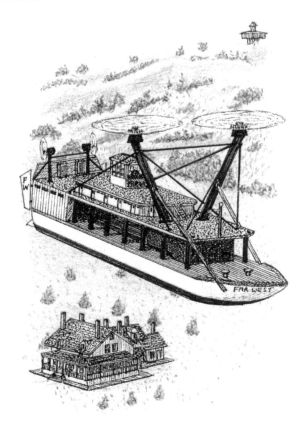

"Remember Grant Marsh!" in multi-colored lights.

Suddenly, the lights changed and began flashing something else—**Where are we going next? Taiwan Scone!**

"Taiwan Scone?" said KT with a puzzled look. "What's that?"

"Sounds like a breakfast treat," said Chad, chuckling.

"Well, Sarabiskota," said Prez. "I have no idea who's responsible for this—but I think we have another mystery on our hands."

As they watched, the *Far West* flew to the west—over the same hills Custer and his men had marched on their way to Montana 150 years earlier. Soon, it was out of sight.

"That's definitely not something you see every day," Nick said, totally amazed at what he'd just witnessed.

Chapter 8

Solving the Clue

There was a real buzz of excitement on board the hundreds of boats as they all went back up the river to where they'd come from. On board many of the boats, people were using their phones to find out everything they could about Grant Marsh, the *Far West*, and Taiwan Scones, and what it had to do with Ft. Abraham Lincoln. In homes all over the world, people were doing their own research.

On board *Recess Time*, Sarabiskota got into quite a discussion about what they'd just witnessed and what it all meant. Finally, Kevin said, "Prez and Egore, we don't want any help from your two big brains figuring out what this *Taiwan Scone* thing means unless we get desperate."

"That's okay with me," said Egore.

"Me too," said Prez. "Egore and I will keep Nick's dad company while the rest of you can see if you can figure out what *Taiwan Scone* refers to."

***

About 15 minutes later, the eight members of Sarabiskota came back, all excited.

"We've got it!" said Nick.

"It was pretty easy," said KT. "Taiwan Scone is an anagram for *Isaac Newton*."

"Isaac Newton?" said Prez. "You mean the brilliant mathematician and scientist who lived in the 17th and 18th centuries? How does he have anything to do with Captain Grant Marsh?"

Doc explained, "The *Isaac Newton* we're talking is a steamboat that was named after *Captain* Isaac Newton, who built a bunch of steamboats. His son was pretty famous, too, and had the same name. He was the chief engineer on the *USS Monitor*, the Union iron-hulled steamship that took on the ironclad *Merrimac* during the Civil War."

"Impressive," said Prez.

"But wait until you hear the best part about Isaac Newton," said Nick. "Tell them, Kari."

Kari said, "The *Isaac Newton* steamboat just happens to be a huge steamboat that Grant Marsh used to watch from the shore when he was growing up in Rochester, Pennsylvania—near *Pittsburgh*."

"Pittsburgh!" Prez exclaimed. "Grant Marsh grew up near Pittsburgh?"

"Yup," said Kari. "Rochester is only about 20 miles away."

"Here's a drawing of the steamboat *Isaac Newton*," said Kevin, showing it to Egore and Prez on his phone.

Isaac Newton drawing by Samuel Ward Stanton, *Author's Collection*

"It's *huge!*" Prez exclaimed.

"It was," said Chad. "To be exact, it was 338 feet long and 40 feet wide. A football field is 300 feet long and 160 feet wide, so the ship was 38 feet longer than a football field and one-fourth its width."

"And the *Far West* was 190 feet long and only 33 feet wide," Jesssie recalled.

Mike said, "The *Isaac Newton's* paddlewheels were *gigantic*—39 feet in diameter. You could get 1,000 passengers on board the boat. There was a big saloon on board with a giant dome over the whole thing—and the dome was made of stained and painted glass."

"So, whatever happened to the *Isaac Newton?*" asked Prez.

"It had its share of accidents," Jessie answered. "But it all ended on December 3, 1863, when one of the boilers exploded."

"Was anyone killed?" Prez wanted to know.

"There were 14 killed and 17 injured," Jessie answered. "But it was really lucky that it was late in the season and there weren't a lot of passengers on board—

plus two other boats were nearby and they quickly rescued lots of people."

"So, do you guys think this clue means what I think it means?" asked Prez.

"Yup!" Chad exclaimed. "It looks like we're going to Pittsburgh!"

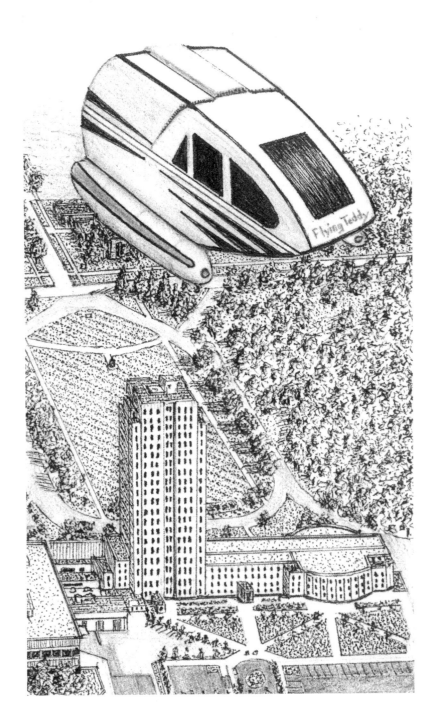

CHAPTER 9

Getting Organized

When Sarabiskota got back to Nick's parents' cabin, they immediately got on board the *Flying Teddy*.

"Let's do a quick fly-over of the area before we head to the airport," said Prez.

Doc asked, "What are we going to do after we get back to the *Exercise?*"

"Maybe eat a snack and settle down a bit," said Prez. "Then, let's divide into groups and do some research and get organized. Kari, would you do your magic and get us organized?"

"I've already been thinking about this," said Kari. "Egore and Prez, maybe you could try to gather all the video and photos you can get from this incident and analyze it. It will be great to have it for historical purposes, but there also might be some clues as to who's behind this Grant Marsh-*Far West* mystery. Post some of the best stuff on our Spacebook page if you have time."

"Sounds good," said Egore.

"Excellent idea," Prez added.

Kari continued, "KT and Kevin, how 'bout you two do an overview of the Steamboat Era for us. I think we need a little historical background."

"Okay," KT and Kevin said at the same time.

"Doc and Chad, maybe you can start working on a brief overview of Grant Marsh's life."

"Will do," said Doc.

"Good idea," said Chad.

Kari said, "Mike and I will start working on all the arrangements for a trip to Pittsburgh plus we will have to cancel our plans for Australia."

"Please see if there's a baseball game going on the next day or two in Pittsburgh," said Kevin. "It would be great if we could see a Pirates games while we're there."

"I'm on it," said Mike.

"That leaves you, Nick and Jessie," said Kari. "Maybe you two could start compiling some of the best stories about Captain Marsh. Be ready to tell us one or two."

"That will be fun," said Nick.

"I like that," said Jessie.

CHAPTER 10

The Steamboat Era

Sarabiskota was too keyed up to rest by the time they got back to the *Exercise*. Instead, they got right to work for the next two hours, then they gathered around the Steelers Lounge.

"So? Are we ready to get started?" asked Kari. "KT and Kevin, you're first. Please give us a brief review of the Steamboat Era in the United States."

"There's so much stuff that was new and interesting," said Kevin, "so these are just some highlights. If any of you come up with questions we can't answer, we'll look into them."

KT said. "Now ... let's start by taking a look at this map."

Kevin projected a large map on the wall in front of them.

"This is what America looked like in the early 1800's," KT explained. "Remember, the Lewis and Clark Expedition took place from 1804 to 1806. Many people

Early 1800s

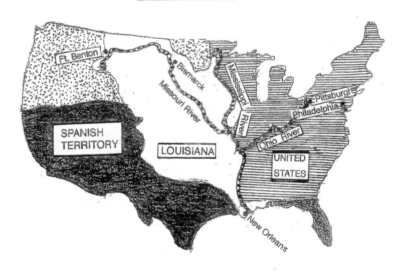

moved west after that, and there was lots of fur trading going on. After that, many more people moved west to look for gold or to try to find a better place to live."

"And with that move westward," Kevin continued, "there was a need to transport people and supplies and stuff from one place to another—and the best way to do that for most of the 1800s—before the railroads took over around the 1880s—was the steamboat."

"What about a wagon train?" asked Nick.

"It was less safe and more difficult," Kevin replied. "Of course, sometimes they had to travel by wagon because the rivers don't flow everywhere."

KT said, "If you look at the map, you'll notice there was a continuous water highway you could take all the way from Pittsburgh, Pennsylvania, to way over here in the west in Ft. Benton, Montana, following the Ohio, Mississippi, and Missouri Rivers. Steamboats were operating all over these rivers during the Steamboat Era, carrying people and supplies and animals."

"How far is it from Pittsburgh to Ft. Benton by river?" asked Chad.

"About 3,400 miles," Kevin answered. "With all the dams that have been built, you couldn't make that trip by steamboat anymore."

"Just think," said KT, "Captain Grant Marsh was alive from 1834 until 1916. That covers most of the Steamboat Era which lasted from about 1807 until the 1880s. Besides that, Captain Marsh worked on all three of those major rivers during his lifetime."

"Was it Fulton who invented the steamboat?" asked Mike.

Kevin answered, "Actually, we found out Robert

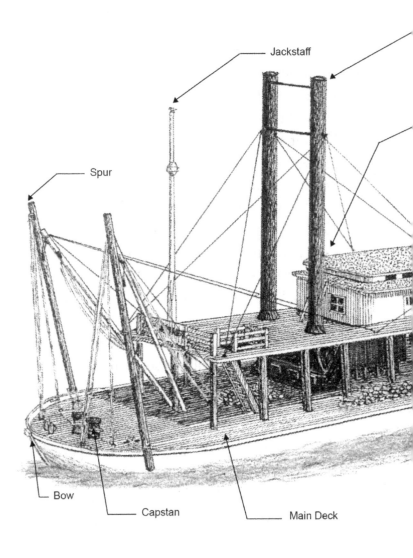

Jackstaff

Spur

Bow

Capstan

Main Deck

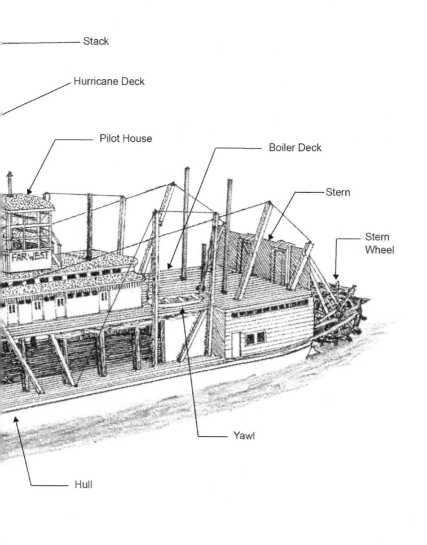

Stack

Hurricane Deck

Pilot House

Boiler Deck

Stern

Stern Wheel

FAR WEST

Yawl

Hull

Fulton built the first *commercially successful* steamboat—in other words, the first steamboat to make a profit. It took passengers from Albany to New York City and back in 1807. I think it was John Fitch who invented the steamboat in the 1780s."

KT said, "Next, we have a diagram of the *Far West* showing some of the parts of a steamboat."

Kevin projected the diagram onto the wall.

"Let me go over a few of these," said Kevin. "You probably know many of them already. Remember, the front of the boat is the *bow* and the back is the *stern*. The body of the ship is the *hull*. There were three decks on the *Far West*. The *main deck* was the one closest to the water and all the boilers and machinery were on that deck. Above that, was the *boiler deck*, and that's where the passengers' cabins were. Above that was the *hurricane deck*."

"Why did they call it the *hurricane deck*?" asked Kari.

"It was the uppermost deck and it was a great place to get a nice breeze—not quite as strong as a hurricane, but you get the point," said Kevin.

"Cool," said Kari.

KT said, "A *yawl* was a rowboat that they could use for things like going to get wood when the steamboat needed it."

"Or maybe to go fishing," Chad suggested.

"That's right," said KT.

"The *capstan* was a winch so they could pull in heavy lines and stuff," said KT. "The *jackstaff* was a tall pole that was on the bow or front of the steamboat. The pilot could look out from the pilot house, and the jackstaff would give him a reference point for maneuvering the boat."

"Where was the bathroom?" asked Jessie.

Kevin chuckled. "It was in the back of the boat and they called it a *privy*."

Prez chuckled. "I'm guessing the privy on the *Far West* wasn't nearly as nice as the ones on board the *Exercise*."

"You can be sure of that," said Jessie.

"The *pilot house*, of course, was where Captain Marsh would have steered the boat," said KT.

"Is the captain the same thing as the pilot?" asked Mike.

"That's something we were confused about, too," said Kevin. "The *pilot* of a steamboat was considered much more important than the captain and got paid a lot more, too. The pilot was responsible for navigating the boat, and the *captain* managed the business part. Some men like Grant Marsh did both jobs on the steamboat."

"The pilots were like the superstars of the time," said KT. "Grant Marsh mentioned making $950 in one month on one of his jobs on the Missouri River, much more than any other steamboat pilot had ever made. That's about $20,000 in today's money."

"Wow!" Mike exclaimed.

"Were there any women pilots?" asked Doc.

"We didn't find any yet," KT answered.

"What's the deal with the *paddlewheel*?" asked Doc. "Why didn't they use propellers?"

"Steamboats needed to operate in rivers that were shallow in many areas," Kevin explained. "Paddlewheels were much better in those conditions. You'll notice the *Far West* had its paddlewheel in the back, and it was called a *sternwheeler.* Other steamboats had their paddlewheel on the side, and they were called *sidewheelers.* I read that the sternwheelers were better on the Missouri River because the hull of the boat protected the paddlewheel from most of the floating logs and other stuff in the Missouri."

KT continued, "We found out that when Captain Marsh was working on the Missouri River, it was a wild and crazy river. It was nicknamed the *Big Muddy* and the *Big Misery,* and it was described as fickle, dangerous, treacherous, and impetuous. Many steamboat pilots didn't even want to work on the river. Steamboats were lucky to last three or four years. It's pretty amazing! Grant Marsh never lost a steamboat on the Missouri."

"Did he ever lose a steamboat on another river?" asked Nick.

"I'm not sure," said Kevin.

"We'll find out," said KT.

"How many steamboats sank and stuff on the Missouri River?" asked Nick.

"There were 289 confirmed sinkings, but more than that were probably lost," said Kevin. "Take a wild guess what sank most of them."

"The steam engines blew up?" Mike guessed.

"No, but good guess," Kevin replied.

"They got stuck on sandbars?" Chad guessed.

"No, but another good guess."

"Collisions?" Kari guessed.

"No again."

"How about fires?"

"No."

"Big ice chunks?"

"No, but that happened, and some steamboats got iced-in and they were destroyed that way."

Kevin looked over at Egore for the answer. "Snags," he said.

"What exactly is that?" asked Nick.

Kevin said, "It's what happens when you have a floating tree trunk in the river, and one end gets stuck in the mud and sand and then the other end sticks up at an angle. Then a steamboat comes along and—"

"Hole in the boat!" said Prez.

"That's right," said KT. "Remember, the boat was mostly made of wood."

Kevin said, "They actually had boats called *snagboats* to take the snags out of the river, but there were so many snags and not enough snagboats. We found out one of the snagboats was even named the *Mandan*. Here's what the *Mandan* looked like."

THE SNAGBOAT *MANDAN*; OVERHOLSER HISTORICAL RESEARCH CENTER, FORT BENTON, MT

"Cool," said Mike. "Could we get back to the sandbars for just a second. How could they possibly get a big steamboat off a sandbar if it got stuck on it really good."

"You'll like this," said Kevin. "It is a tough one to explain, but let me show you a photo that will help you visualize how it worked. Grant Marsh called it *sparring* a boat, but it became known as *grasshoppering* because the boat had to move in little hops over the sandbar—like a grasshopper. I've got a great illustration to show you that will give you an idea of how it worked without getting into all the gory details."

Kevin projected the illustration onto the wall.

"Whoever came up with that was a genius," said Chad.

"The steamboat actually looks a lot like a big grasshopper when they were doing that," Doc added.

"What happened if that didn't work?" asked Jessie.

"Then the steamboat was probably done for," said Kevin. "Then another steamboat would come along and try to salvage what could be saved."

"Prez," said KT. "You're not going to believe what I'm going to tell you next, but your *second* favorite president, Abraham Lincoln, actually invented another way to lift boats over sandbars besides grasshoppering. He even got a patent for it, but his invention was never used."

"No way!" said Prez.

"Yes, he did," said KT. "Here's a photo of a model showing his idea. He's actually the only president to ever get a patent."

"Unbelievable!" said Prez.

"Lincoln actually worked on his invention when he was in the United States Congress in 1848," KT explained. "His idea involved ropes and pulleys that helped inflate bellows on the side of the boat to lift the boat up when it hit the sand."

"What are bellows?" asked Nick.

Kevin said, "They were like flexible bags that air could be drawn into or moved out. The accordion that Lawrence Welk played is a good example of bellows used in a different way."

"Cool," said Nick.

KT said, "We found out Lincoln even took a flatboat down the Ohio and Mississippi Rivers when he was just a teenager. He actually experienced being in a steamboat when it was stuck on a sandbar, and it was then that he started thinking about a way to solve the problem."

"Just another reason to love Abraham Lincoln," said Chad.

"This just keeps getting more and more interesting," said Mike. "What did they do for fun on the steamboats?"

ABRAHAM LINCOLN'S INVENTION, *AUTHOR'S COLLECTION*

KT said, "Grant Marsh mentioned that the second most important person on the steamboat after the pilot was the barkeeper, so that might give you some idea. They played lots of poker and other games in that bar and on the boat. I also read about the fact that conversations with the pilot were a big pastime."

Kevin said, "I read about some kids playing on the sandbars. Passengers also liked to shoot at geese and ducks, go fishing, watch out for animals, and look out for American Indians."

Prez giggled. "Sounds like you would have been bored, Chad."

"For sure," said Chad. "I can't even imagine what it would have been like. It must have been pretty crowded on board those steamboats, too."

"It was," said KT.

"How many people worked on the steamboats?" Nick wanted to know.

"It depended on how big the boat was—also how much freight and how many passengers had to be taken care of," KT replied. "The crew on a smaller steamboat like the *Far West* would be about 40."

Kevin looked at his notes and said, "You already know about the captain and pilot, but there were a lot of other men working on the steamboats. There were *engineers* to make sure the steam engines worked, *clerks* to keep track of the goods and stuff on board, there was a *steward* to keep track of the waiters and cooks, *carpenters* to fix the boat when needed, and *strikers* who did the dirty work for the engineers. The *deckhands* were the ones who did all the stuff like manning the lines and keeping the boat ship-shape. The *roustabouts* loaded the wood and freight, and the *mates* supervised the deckhands and roustabouts."

"How much wood did it take to keep the steamboats' engines running?" asked Prez.

KT said, "Grant Marsh said it took about 25 cords of hardwood or 30 cords of cottonwood to run his steamboat for 24 hours. But he actually talked about some bigger boats that used a *lot* more wood than that."

"What's a cord?" Nick asked.

"Picture a stack of wood four feet high by four feet wide and eight feet long," said Kevin. "That's a cord."

"That's a lot of wood," said Mike. "How much did it cost?"

"About eight dollars," answered Kevin. "According to a chart we found, that would be more than $200 in today's money."

"Wow!" said Jessie.

"This was pretty funny," said Kevin. "Grant Marsh told about a huge steamboat called the *Nebraska* that was on the way to New Orleans and needed 100 cords of wood on board. It actually had 15 boilers, and it needed lots of wood to burn for fuel. When it pulled up to a landing for wood, it had to keep the engines running—just to keep it a safe distance from the landing. Well, the engines were so inefficient and used so much wood, they used up all the wood before the boat was even ready to leave."

"Wow! That's poor wood mileage," Nick said, laughing.

KT said, "Grant Marsh talked about the people selling wood to the steamboats along the lower Missouri River called wood hawks. As they got into the upper Missouri River region, there were fewer of these *wood hawks*, so they sometimes had to find piles of driftwood called *rack heaps* that the river's current had piled up on sandbars. There were also *deadenings*, which were trees that were still standing after fires."

Kevin added, "But when they had to leave their steamboats to get wood, there were definitely some risks. In 1868, there were seven wood-choppers killed by Sioux Indians in the upper Missouri River area."

"They had a last resort for wood for the steamboats— green cottonwood trees," said KT, "but they didn't burn well at all."

"There are some great stories about some of the wood hawks that Grant Marsh knew," said Kevin. "This

74

one guy was named "X" Beidler, a big tough guy."

"Sounds like a good name for a professional wrestler," said Chad.

"It does," said Kevin. "We actually found a photo of him."

Kevin projected the photo onto the wall.

"I think I could handle him in a wrestling match," said Chad.

"You're a dreamer, Chad," said Egore.

Everyone laughed.

"X" Beidler; *Overholser Historical Research Center, Fort Benton, MT*

CHAPTER 11

Overview of Grant Marsh's Life

"All right, Doc and Chad," said Kari. "You're next. Give us a brief overview of Grant Marsh's life."

"I'll start," said Doc. "According to most sources we found, Grant Marsh was born in Rochester, Pennsylvania, on the Ohio River near Pittsburgh on May 11, 1834."

"What do you mean *according to most sources we found*?" asked Nick.

"Well," Doc replied, "when we were looking for Grant Marsh's place of birth, we found at least four different places listed, so we went with the one that was listed in Captain Marsh's biography that was written when he was still alive."

Chad said, "Not only was he still alive when the book was written, but Grant Marsh and the author actually became pretty good friends, and they had several conversations and exchanged many letters before Marsh's biography was finished."

"We've run into conflicting information in historical research before," Kari noted. "But it seems like they could all at least get the birthplace right?"

"Yeah," said Kevin.

Chad continued. "Captain Marsh died on January 2, 1916 in Bismarck, North Dakota, on the Missouri River."

"So, he was born in a river town, died in a river town, and spent most of his life on steamboats on rivers," Jessie observed.

"And Captain Marsh was 81 years, seven months, and 22 days old when he died," said Prez.

"How do you do that so fast in your head?" asked Nick.

"I'm not sure," Prez answered.

"And he was approximately 2,576, 448, 000 seconds old," added Egore.

"I know how *you* do that so fast, Egore," said Kevin with a chuckle.

"What did he die of?" asked KT.

"Pneumonia," Doc answered. "It's basically a serious lung infection. It's especially dangerous for older people because they are often undernourished, and without the proper nutrients, they have a tough time fighting it."

"Thanks, Doc."

"By the way," said Doc. "I checked. The average man back then only lived to be about 46, so Grant Marsh lived way past the average life expectancy."

"Just 46!?" Kari exclaimed. "My dad's just about that age."

"Yup," said Doc. "Medical advances over the past 100 to 200 years have made a huge difference."

"It was much more dangerous living in America at that time," added Kevin.

"For sure," said Doc.

Chad said, "We found out that in 1830, just four years before Grant Marsh was born, there were about 200 steamboats on the western rivers, and most of them were actually built in the Pittsburgh and Cincinnati areas. We can't verify it yet, but we think Grant Marsh's dad actually worked in a shipbuilding plant."

"The *Far West* was even built in Pittsburgh," said Doc. "And there was another interesting thing we discovered about Pittsburgh that might be a little off topic. We noticed the spelling of Pittsburgh was not consistent in our research. Several sources didn't have the "h" at the end."

"What was the deal?" asked KT.

"You'll like this," Chad said with a big smile. "The confusion started out as a printer's error in 1816, which resulted in lots of confusion. The confusion just got worse in 1890 when a government board called the United States Board of Geographical Names made all cities ending in "burgh" drop the "h". Then, in 1911, that same board let Pittsburgh have their "h" back."

"Too funny," said Prez. "I'm glad they got it back."

"How much do you know about Grant Marsh's family?" asked Jessie.

"Quite a bit," answered Doc, "Grant Marsh's parents were named John and Lydia. So far, we found the names of three sisters and two brothers, but we're not sure how reliable this information is. From oldest to youngest there was Catharine, Amanda, then Grant, Robert or Russ, Lydia, and James or Monroe."

"Anything interesting about them?" asked Kevin.

"There were a lot of steamboat men among them and the people they married," answered Doc. "For example, Catharine married a steamboat pilot named Robert Gordon. Amanda married a steamboat steward named John Gordon. Russ was a steamboat steward who was on many of Grant Marsh's boats. Lydia married a steamboat pilot named William Gordon. Monroe was a steamboat engineer."

"Lots of Gordons in the family," Egore noted.

"Did Grant Marsh have any kids?" asked Mike.

"Yes," Doc answered, looking over at Katy and smiling.

"What!?" KT exclaimed.

Doc explained, "Grant Marsh married a lady named Katy, and he mentions them having *five* children, but we found six names listed one place. Again, we'll have to dig into the sources when we have more time. From the oldest to the youngest, the kids' names we found were John, Grant, Caroline or Carrie, Nellie, Katheryne or Kate, and Lillian or Lillie."

"I definitely like *Kate* the best," said KT with a chuckle.

Doc said, "Here's what we could find out about them in a short period of time. Lillie died in her early twenties when she was a schoolteacher. John was a steamboat pilot like his dad. Grant C. was a riverboat captain. Carrie was married to a steamboat man and hotel steward, and Nellie was married to a railroad auditor."

"What about Kate?" asked KT.

"Oh, sorry," said Doc with a smile. "Her husband was a steamboat pilot named Robert Gaines."

"I knew she would marry a prominent man," said KT with a giggle.

"But then something must have happened to Robert, and Kate married a grocery store guy named William Roper after that," Doc said.

KT giggled. "At least she *always* had fresh fruits and veggies."

"Enough, KT," said Chad, chuckling. "From the time Captain Marsh was 12, when he became a cabin boy on a steamboat called the *Dover,* he spent about 70 years on steamboats somewhere on the three large rivers we talked about before—the Ohio, the Mississippi, and the Missouri."

"And he spent most his time on the Missouri River, right?" asked Nick.

"Yes."

"What's a cabin boy do again?" Nick asked.

"Mostly run errands for the captain and others on the steamboat," Doc answered.

Kevin said, "Hey, I noticed they kept calling many of the steamboats that Captain Marsh was on *packets.* What's that?"

"I looked it up and those were just steamboats that carried both freight and passengers," Chad answered.

Doc said, "Grant Marsh found his way to the Missouri River pretty quickly, and he was still a teenager when he first started working on the river. From what we read so far, it was easy to tell that the river got into Grant Marsh's blood from the time he was a little kid, playing down by the river. Then when he was 12, he got that job as cabin boy on the *Dover* on the Allegheny River between Pittsburgh and Freeport, Pennsylvania. In 1852, when he was just 18, he was a deckhand on the packet *Beaver* that went from Pittsburgh to St. Louis. By the spring of 1854, when he was still 19, he was a deckhand on the *F.X. Aubrey* that went from St. Louis to St. Joseph, Missouri. That was the first time he worked on a boat on the Missouri River."

Kari asked, "Did you find the names of the other steamboats Captain Marsh worked on during his life?"

Chad said, "Yes, but we're not sure if it was a complete list. There were more than 30 names on it."

"What were your favorites?" asked Egore.

"My favorite steamboat name was *Silver Lake*, and my second-favorite was *Little Eagle*," said Doc.

"How about you, Chad?"

"My favorite was *North Eclipse* and my second-favorite was *Deer Lodge*."

"What did Grant Marsh look like?" asked Prez.

"We found this drawing of him," said Doc, projecting it onto the wall in front of them.

Chad said, "His biographer used these words to describe him: *tall; broad-shouldered, with a powerful frame; clear-eyed, with a gentle voice.*"

"What's clear-eyed mean?" asked Kevin.

"That means he had practical cleverness and judgement. He was insightful," Prez answered.

"I think I could have handled him in a race or a good wrestling match," said Chad confidently.

"I doubt it, Chad," said Jessie. "Nick and I have a story to tell you that will give you an idea what kind of shape Grant Marsh was in."

"All right, Nick and Jessie," Kari said. "Let's have you tell your stories next."

"We've got two ready," said Jessie. "One is a little *gross*, and the other will give Chad an idea what kind of physical condition Grant Marsh was in."

"Which story would you like to hear first?" asked Nick.

CHAPTER 12

Surprise Feast and Fast Walker

"Okay," Jessie began, "Our first story takes place in 1868, so Grant Marsh was about 34 years old. By this time he had been married to Katy for eight years and they were living in St. Louis. It was the middle of the summer, and the captain had already made one trip on the Missouri River—from St. Louis up to Ft. Benton and back—on the steamboat *Nile*."

Nick continued, "Captain Marsh figured it was too late to make another round trip up there and back because it would be fall before he got back, and icy conditions and low water on the Missouri River would make it dangerous. So, instead of heading back to Ft. Benton, he decided he would do some work on the lower Missouri River closer to home in St. Louis, where winter conditions wouldn't set in until later."

"Then something happened," said Jessie. "Late in the summer, he got a request from the United States

Government to head up here to a place about 86 miles south of Ft. Rice."

Jessie pointed out the location on a map.

"What was the deal?" asked Prez.

"Well," said Nick, "apparently there was a United States Government treaty with Chief Red Cloud of the Ogallala Sioux Tribe. As part of that treaty, the government had to set up facilities, including schools, for the tribe. The government was pretty anxious to do their part before the winter, and if anyone could do the job, it would be Grant Marsh."

"He didn't make it there, did he?" KT guessed.

"I'm not going to answer that question yet," said Nick. "But they didn't even leave St. Louis on the *Nile* until October 15, and you know how cold it can get in October in North Dakota. When they finally left, Captain Marsh was pretty sure he wasn't going to finish the trip before his boat was frozen in the ice or worse."

Jessie continued, "The water was low when they were traveling up the river, and the cargo weighed a lot, so they couldn't go very fast. They got right here to a place called Cal-de-Sac Island, and they had to take part of the cargo and leave it on the island. After that, they got up the Missouri River another 50 miles or so when the ice started flowing in the river. Captain Marsh realized he had to turn back. They put the rest of the cargo at a place near the Cheyenne River, then turned back, trying to get away before they were frozen in. Captain Marsh knew that no riverboat had ever made it through a winter frozen in the ice."

"Why not?" asked Mike.

"Imagine being stuck in the ice in a boat made of wood with hostile Sioux Indians around," said Jessie.

"How far did they get?" Kevin asked.

"Just a little bit south of where Chamberlain, South Dakota is," said Nick. "Captain Marsh was able to guide The Nile to the eastern bank of the Missouri River, as far away from the Sioux Indians as he could get."

"Did *The Nile* get attacked?" Doc wanted to know.

"No," Nick answered, "but just try to imagine being stuck on a steamboat all winter. Talk about cabin fever! The captain and the crew could hike 25 miles to Ft. Thompson and pick up supplies to break the monotony, and that's where the interesting and funny part of the story begins. … You see, there was a guy at Ft. Thompson named Jud Lamoure. He liked Captain Marsh—but you won't believe what he did to the captain and his brother Monroe, who was working as an engineer on the *Nile*. It's pretty funny but also pretty gross. … Anyway, Lamoure invited Captain Marsh and Monroe Marsh for a feast of venison at Ft. Thompson. The fort had run out of its supply of meat a long time before this, so Grant and Monroe really enjoyed the feast. But … they also noticed Jud Lamoure wasn't eating the deer meat they were eating—he was only eating *bacon*."

Jessie continued. "So they asked him *why* he wasn't eating the venison, and he said he was just tired of it."

"It was actually buffalo poop, wasn't it?" Kevin asked, grimacing.

"Ewwwwwwwwwww!"

"Gross!"

"It turned out to be more than gross," Jessie said. "Thirty-eight years later, in 1906, when Grant Marsh was living in Bismarck, he found out what he and Monroe had been eating. He was at home reading *The Bismarck*

Tribune newspaper when he found a story where Jud Lamoure was describing that feast—and practical joke— on the steamboat *Nile* with Grant and Monroe Marsh. … It was a *dog* feast."

"Ewwwwwwwwwww!"

"Gross!"

"Disgusting!"

Nick said, "Grant Marsh didn't think it was funny at all, either. He couldn't wait to get his hands on Lamoure—but I guess it never happened."

Jessie said, "That wasn't the only trick Lamoure and his buddies played on Captain Marsh that winter, either. And that gets us to our second story."

"I hope it doesn't involve more eating," said Mike, grimacing.

"No, it involves *exercise*," said Jessie. "You see, Captain Marsh liked to check on the stuff he had left on Cal-de-Sac Island, but it was 47 miles away and two-thirds of that distance involved walking on land. It was really dangerous to go all that way alone, so Captain Marsh would meet someone along the way at Crew Creek, and then they'd walk together."

Nick continued, "Captain Marsh was in really good shape, and this was the time when walking contests were a big thing in the eastern part of the country. Captain Marsh was an excellent speed-walker, and after he walked together with someone for a while, he used to leave his walking partners way behind. Jud Lamoure and some of the other men at the fort found out about this, and they decided to play another trick on Captain Marsh—they would find someone who was faster than Grant Marsh that would leave *him* in the dust."

"So," said Jessie, "the first guy they found to challenge Grant Marsh was named Bad Moccasin, and he turned out to be a real loser. Grant Marsh left him way behind after just a few miles."

"Maybe he needed better moccasins," said Egore.

Everyone laughed.

Jessie said, "Grant Marsh may have handled Bad Moccasin easily, but that just made Jud and his buddies even more determined to find someone to beat Captain Marsh."

"Who did they find next?" asked Kari, loving the story so far.

"They found a guy named Dutch Jake," said Nick, "a guy who worked at Ft. Thompson. He claimed to be the fastest walker in the West. He definitely was a better opponent for Captain Marsh. In fact, when they started out, Grant Marsh had difficulty keeping up. They were basically even until they got to a steep bluff, and that's when Grant Marsh started pulling ahead. By the time they reached Ft. Thompson, Grant Marsh was leading by two miles."

"Dutch Jake couldn't handle the hills," said Kevin. "A little like Chad."

"Hey! Everyone has their weaknesses," Chad whined.

"And Jud and the others didn't give up after that either, I'll bet," said KT.

"You are correct, KT," said Nick. "The third challenger was a Brule Sioux Indian who had a name that turned out to be well-deserved—*Fast Walker*. Let's just say he was 130 pounds of muscle and endurance and speed. The best of the best."

"I think I could beat him!" Chad said, then everyone groaned.

"Only Egore could have beaten this man," said Jessie.

"How fast was he?" asked Chad.

"He may have been unbeatable," Nick answered. "After all this happened, Captain Marsh saw him beat a thoroughbred horse on a race from Ft. Thompson to a creek 24 miles away. The horse led the first 10 miles, then Fast Walker caught him and passed him for good."

"Captain Marsh didn't have a chance against Fast Walker," said Jessie. "The speedy American Indian took the lead right away and extended it farther. At the end of three hours, Grant Marsh watched in amazement as Fast Walker disappeared over the horizon."

Nick said, "It's pretty cool, because Fast Walker and Captain Marsh actually became really good friends after that. In fact, Fast Walker used to visit Captain Marsh for several days during the summers and camp in his yard."

"That's a really cool story," said Egore.

"Yeah," said KT.

"It gets even better," said Jessie. "Several years after this, Captain Marsh wrote to his friend Buffalo Bill and told him he should get Fast Walker to be part of his famous Wild West Show and have him race the best speed walkers from the East. Buffalo Bill sent a letter back saying no one would *dare* take Fast Walker on. They would all lose for sure."

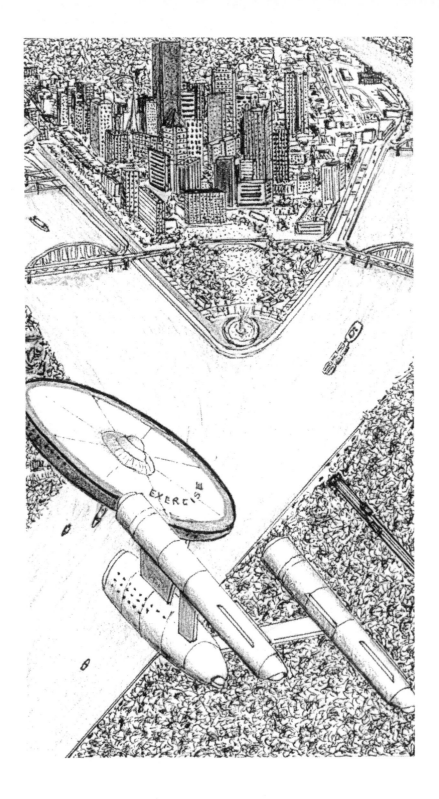

CHAPTER 13

Arriving In Pittsburgh

The *Exercise* attracted lots of attention as it flew at a low altitude over the Pittsburgh area and then approached the Pittsburgh International Airport. There was no aircraft in the world more unique and recognizable than the *Exercise.*

As they approached for a landing, Nick was first to notice the large crowd that had gathered near the private plane terminal. "I think we have a welcoming party," he said.

"This should be fun," said Mike.

As soon as they got off the *Exercise*, two other part-owners of the Pittsburgh Steelers were the first to greet them. These particular owners also happened to be two of the greatest Pittsburgh Steelers of all-time—Jack Lambert and Troy Polymollydoo.

"Jack! Troy!" Sarabiskota called out when they saw their two good friends.

"So good to see you all!" Jack Lambert replied as he

greeted them all with big hugs.

"Hi everyone!" Troy said, smiling, as he walked over and hugged everyone.

"We got your tentative schedule from Kari," Jack said. "Starting out your day with sandwiches at Primanti Brothers is a good choice. Good news—Troy and I got you great seats for the Pirates game tonight."

"Thanks!"

Troy said, "If it's all right, Jack and I want to hang out with you today as much as you'll let us. We hope you have room for us on the *Flying Teddy* when you fly over the area."

"We always have room for you two," said Egore.

"That's right," said Prez. "We love having you guys around."

"Great," said Jack. "I'm really enjoying all this Grant Marsh stuff so far."

"Me too," said Troy. "Oh, looks like there's lots of press over here to talk to you before we catch our limo."

Sarabiskota, Jack, and Troy all had big smiles as they approached a cheering crowd. They stopped when they got to a podium with several microphones mounted on it.

"We're so happy to be here!" said Prez. "We love Pittsburgh! ... Go Pirates! Go Penguins! Go STEELERS!"

The crowd cheered.

"Prez, what do you think's going to happen here today?" a reporter from Channel 11 called out.

"We are just like the rest of you," Prez answered. "We have no idea, but we can't wait to find out. After what happened last night, we expect something pretty special is going to happen here in the Pittsburgh area today related to Captain Grant Marsh. After all, he was born around here, and many of the steamboats he worked on were built right here in Pittsburgh—including the *Far West*."

"Kari, do you guys have any idea at all who's responsible for what happened yesterday in North Dakota?" asked a reporter from Channel 4.

"We have no clue," Kari answered, "but we're all finding this to be very interesting and intriguing. In case anyone's interested, we're posting everything we're finding out about Grant Marsh on Spacebook."

"Mike, where are you headed right now?" a Channel 2 reporter asked.

There were some screams from among the ladies as Mike got close to the microphones to speak.

"Right now, our plans are to get a sandwich at Primanti Brothers then we're going to fly over the area on the *Flying Teddy*. Later, we plan on taking a cruise on the steamboat *Immaculate Reception* then we're going to the Pirates game tonight. Our plans will change if anything significant happens."

"Troy and Jack, are you going to accompany Sarabiskota?" a newspaper reporter asked.

A huge cheer went up from the crowd when Troy and Jack approached the microphones. "Let's go STEELERS! Let's go STEELERS!" the crowd chanted.

"Yes, we're going to hang out with Sarabiskota as much as they'll let us," Troy said with a big smile. "This is a lot of fun for us."

"Like all of you, we don't know what to expect," added Jack. "But we want to be close to the action. Doesn't this feel a little like a Super Bowl atmosphere in Pittsburgh today? This is great!"

The crowd cheered again. Then they chanted, "Let's go STEELERS! ... Let's go, STEELERS! ... Let's go STEELERS!

***

It was a little crazy at Primanti Brothers, as thousands of people wanted to meet Sarabiskota and two of the Steelers' greatest players.

JB and Madison mingled in with the large crowd, enjoying everything going on. They were both holding plates with large sandwiches on them, trying to eat them while standing up.

Madison said, "I would never have thought about putting French fries and coleslaw on a sandwich, but I like it. Why do they call it *Terry* coleslaw?"

JB giggled. "It's to honor one of the Pittsburgh Steelers' great quarterbacks, Terry *Bradshaw*."

"Bradshaw—Coleslaw. That's funny," said Madison, giggling.

JB said, "Hey, don't you think the Sarabiskota boys are even cuter in person than their photos—especially Prez? And the girls are really cute too."

"I agree with you about the girls, but I think Kevin is the cutest boy," said Madison. Then she whispered into JB's ear, "I think everyone's going to love it when they see our next Grant Marsh extravaganza."

JB whispered back, "If everything works the way we planned it."

"Oh, it will," Madison whispered.

***

In the afternoon, Troy, Jack, and Sarabiskota were up in the *Flying Teddy*, flying all over the Pittsburgh area. When they got over Rochester, where Grant Marsh was born, Jack said, "Troy and I have been reading up and reviewing everything you posted about Grant Marsh on Spacebook. We actually found a couple of other things you might find interesting. We got over to Rochester, Pennsylvania, this morning before we left for the airport to meet you. As you all know, that was Grant Marsh's birthplace. Anyway, there's an old cemetery there where Grant Marsh's parents are buried. We went in there and took this photo of the gravestone. It was in a prominent place, right near the front gate."

PHOTO COURTESY OF MICHELLE LONG, ROCHESTER AREA HISTORICAL SOCIETY, ROCHESTER, PA

"That's awesome!" said Prez.

"We also found an artist's depiction of what the area looked like about the time Grant Marsh lived there," said Jack. "It's pretty cool."

PHILLIPSBURG   SOLDIERS   ORPHAN   SCHOOL.   REV. W. G. TAYLOR D. D. PRIN
WATER CURE P. O. BEAVER Co PA

PHOTO COURTESY OF THE BEAVER COUNTY HISTORICAL RESEARCH AND LANDMARKS ASSOCIATION, PA

"That's so beautiful," said Jessie.

Nick said, "It *almost* makes me wish I could have lived back in that time, but—"

"No A&B Pizza!" Nick's Sarabiskota friends shouted.

Everyone laughed. "Did you two find anything about Grant Marsh's life as a kid?" asked Doc.

"Not much," said Troy. "We read what you wrote on Spacebook about Grant Marsh and his friends playing by the river, throwing rocks at the *Isaac Newton* steamboat."

Jack added, "It's hard to imagine he was working on steamboats at age 12. I think I was still in diapers at that age."

Everyone laughed.

"It sure was a different time," said Doc. "I'd love to go back in time and spend a few days with a young Grant Marsh and see what his days were like. Can you even *imagine?*"

"That would be awesome," said Jessie.

KT said, "I'll bet Grant Marsh at any age would have been totally freaked out if he'd seen what happened on the Missouri River last night."

"That's a sure bet," said Chad. "I can't wait to see what's going to happen *next.*"

CHAPTER 14

On the Way to the Pirates Game

Troy, Jack, and Sarabiskota had a fun day in the Pittsburgh area, but nothing happened related to Grant Marsh. While they were on the steamboat going over to PNC Park, where the Pirates play baseball, Prez said, "Egore, do you have another story you could tell us about Grant Marsh?"

"Oh, sure," said Egore, "It's a good story to tell while we're in Pittsburgh because it involves the steamboat *Ida Stockdale* which was actually built in Pittsburgh under Grant Marsh's direction during the winter of 1866. The boat was owned by a Pittsburgh captain, Captain R.S. Calhoun. He had hired Captain Marsh to be in charge of his new steamboat during its first summer season, when it was operating between St. Louis and Ft. Benton on the Missouri River. Calhoun just went along for the ride.

"It was a pretty incredible first season. Captain Calhoun was really happy about all that Captain Marsh and the *Ida Stockdale* accomplished during that time. Keep in mind, there were 39 steamboats that made that Ft. Benton run during that summer. Captain Marsh and the *Ida Stockdale* set the record for profits that year. The boat made $42,594 after all the expenses were paid. That amount would have actually paid for the cost of building the *Ida Stockdale* two times. And Grant Marsh made $1,200 per month, which was a huge salary at the time.

"Anyway, that's not the most interesting thing that happened that summer. That particular thing occurred after the *Ida Stockdale* got to Ft. Benton and was returning to St. Louis with cargo. The steamboat got 220 miles below Ft. Buford when someone shot a cannon!"

"They were being attacked!" Nick exclaimed.

"No, it was just to get their attention. And it did. It turned out, the U.S. Army was working close by, and they were setting up military posts in the area. The man in charge, General Alfred Terry, wanted to hire the *Ida Stockdale* to do some work for the Army right away. Grant Marsh agreed, and their work eventually took the *Ida Stockdale* up the Yellowstone River, about 125 miles from its mouth, when something really *amazing* happened."

"A flying saucer landed on their boat!" Nick blurted out.

"There was a Missouri River mermaid that came out of the water and sang to them," Chad guessed.

"No," said Egore laughing, "I think this was even more amazing. I could give you 100 guesses and you would never get it. About 125 miles north of the mouth of the Yellowstone River, they came to a place called Elk Horn Prairie. This was a place with a beautiful meadow

near the riverbank where lots of animals liked to gather, especially elk. But that's not what kind of animals showed up that day. The *Ida Stockdale* would get the thrill of their lives as an enormous number of one particular kind of animal would end up crossing the river in front of their steamboat for several *hours*, swimming around them, bringing them to a complete stop."

"Large ducks?" Jessie guessed.

"No. Buffalo!" Egore said. "It must have been an incredible sight! Grant Marsh ordered the boat's engines stopped. The buffalo became so thick, it was unreal. Thousands and thousands and thousands of them crossed the river in front of the steamboat, blocking their way. Everyone on the boat was a little scared when some of the buffalo actually became entangled in the paddlewheel, but there was nothing they could do about it. The boat was totally at the mercy of the enormous buffalo herd, moving slowly around them. Just imagine this. Large clouds of dust arose as the huge buffalo herd got out of the river and started walking on the land."

Nick giggled. "Can you imagine if Chad was there, and he burped and started a stampede!"

"That wouldn't have been good at all," said Egore. "But everyone was as quiet as possible. This went on for several hours before the steamboat had a chance to finally get through. After Grant Marsh was finally able to get the steamboat moving again, more and more buffalo just kept on going across that river. Several *hours* after the steamboat was able to pass, they looked back and *still* the buffalo were crossing the river."

"That was an awesome story!" said Prez. "I'd like to know just how many buffalo there were."

"A million or more?" Troy guessed.

"Why am I getting hungry for a good buffalo burger right now?" asked Nick.

"It doesn't take much to get *you* hungry anytime," said Jessie, laughing.

"Whatever happened to the *Ida Stockdale?*" asked Doc.

"Sadly, in April of 1871—it was sunk by ice in Bismarck," replied Egore. "Of course, Grant Marsh was not on it at the time. He never lost a boat on the Missouri River."

CHAPTER 15

Twelve Bare Feet

By the time the Pirates-Cardinals game started, the level of anticipation was off the charts. Everyone was sure they were in store for something pretty spectacular related to Captain Grant Marsh.

The game had an overflow crowd, and millions more watched from all over the world on their computers, phones, and televisions. Meanwhile, Troy, Jack, and Sarabiskota had great seats between home plate and first base.

As the game began, it was difficult, even for the players, to focus on the game. Everyone kept looking up at the sky, especially when an airplane or a bird appeared—but nothing out of the ordinary happened.

After the first few innings, people settled down a little and watched a really good game. The Pirates eventually won, eight to seven, with a game-winning double in the ninth inning. The game ended—and that's when it happened!

A little boy in the crowd was first to see it. He pointed off to the west and shouted, "Look!"

Soon, the whole crowd was pointing at a small blob of multicolored light in the sky to the west—it seemed to be approaching quickly! As it got much closer the next 45 seconds or so, everyone could tell what it was—it was the *Far West*—a lifelike realistic 3-D holographic version of the steamboat, complete with holographic crew, all working like busy bees on board.

Up in the pilot house, Captain Marsh was smiling. He had one hand on the wheel and was waving with the other as the *Far West* holograph soon descended to the baseball field, seeming to cover the entire infield.

"OHHHHHHHHHHHHHHH!" the crowd reacted. For more than 30 seconds, the *Far West* remained. People were totally amazed at how real it seemed—and it appeared to be right in front of them! Suddenly, it went straight up, into the air, and hovered approximately 40 feet above the stadium.

Several crew members emerged from the cabin of the *Far West*, carrying something in their hands. It was fireworks, mostly large rockets. For more than 15 minutes after that, they lit them off, creating the most incredible fireworks display ever seen—but there was no *fire* to those fireworks. They were all 3-D holographic images.

Then the last three rockets were fired off. The first one exploded and the message **"Remember Grant Marsh!"** appeared in the air in all–red letters.

"AWWWWWWW!" the crowd reacted.

The next rocket was lit. It flew up into the air and exploded. **"I'll see you tomorrow!"** appeared in all-blue letters.

"OHHHHHHHHHHH!" was the crowd's reaction.

The third rocket was launched, and it shot into the air and exploded. The images of a bunch of bare feet of various sizes suddenly appeared in the air for ten seconds, then disappeared.

"HUH?!" The crowd was obviously puzzled by what they were seeing.

Jack Lambert turned to Sarabiskota and Troy, "I think I know where we're headed next," he said confidently.

"Really!?" asked Prez, surprised.

"How did you figure that out so quickly?" asked Egore.

"I'll give you a hint," Jack replied. "How many feet appeared in the sky?"

"Twelve, I think," Jessie answered.

"Exactly," said Jack. "Twelve feet. That's the clue."

CHAPTER 16

The Mark Twain Connection

After they left PNC Ballpark, they were on the way to Jack Lambert's home in a stretch limousine.

KT said, "You're a genius, Jack! How did you figure out we're going to St. Louis so quickly?"

"Much of it was pure luck and coincidence," Jack answered. "It was pretty easy, because I was up most of last night reading about Grant Marsh, and I ran across a story about the lifelong friendship between Samuel Clemens and Grant Marsh. I was also doing a little research on why Samuel Clemens chose the Mark Twain pen name."

Nick said, "So the 12 feet has something to do with Samuel Clemens who used the name Mark Twain when he wrote his books?"

"Yes," said Jack. "You see, there was a guy on the steamboat called the *leadsman*. He checked the depth of the water, then he loudly announced it so everyone could keep the boat from getting stuck or something. To determine the depth, the leadsman had what was called a *leadline*, which was a line of rope, 30-feet-long, with a pipe at the end, filled with lead, except for the bottom two inches, which was hollow. Stuff from the riverbed could get in that lower, hollow end of the pipe. Then there were marks along the rope. For example, *Mark One* was six feet above the leadline. *Mark Twain* meant the water was two fathoms deep—or the steamboat was in 12 feet of water—which was a safe depth for steamboats."

"Mark Twain—twelve feet," said Kevin. "Cool!"

"That's right," said Jack. "And Mark Twain, whose real name, of course, was Samuel Clemens, became good friends with Grant Marsh, and their friendship began in St. Louis. In fact, Samuel Clemens saved Grant Marsh's life during the winter of 1858 and 1859 when they worked together in St. Louis. It's a great story! … At that time, Grant Marsh would have been 24, Samuel Clemens, 23. Captain Marsh was only about half a year older than Sam."

"Do you have any photos of the two back then?" asked KT.

"I couldn't find a photo of Grant Marsh at that age," said Jack, "but I did find one of Samuel Clemens when he was pretty young."

He showed the photo to everyone on his phone.

"He was handsome!" said KT.

"Very," added Kari. "But maybe he should get a Steelers cap to wear."

Everyone laughed.

SAMUEL CLEMENS; *AUTHOR'S COLLECTION*

"So anyway," Jack continued, "Grant Marsh was in St. Louis on a steamboat called the *A.B Chambers Number 2*, where he was a mate at the time. That meant he directed all the work of the deckhands and the roustabouts. This was the winter, and steamboats weren't operating north of St. Louis because of ice on the river. But south of St. Louis was usually okay. During this particular winter, Grant Marsh and the *A.B Chambers* were involved in the river trade between St. Louis and New Orleans … and you'll never guess who one of the pilots on board the *A.B. Chambers* was."

"Samuel Clemens!" everyone answered at the same time.

"That's right," said Jack. "So, the *A.B Chambers* leaves St. Louis where there were large chunks of ice floating in the river, making it really tough to navigate. By the next afternoon, they get about 165 miles south of St. Louis, when the steamboat gets grounded near a place called Power's Island."

"Wasn't Samuel Clemens a very good pilot?" Chad asked.

"He was really good, but the problem was he had to guide the boat close to shore to try to avoid all those big chunks of ice in the main channel. Anyway, after they ran aground, it didn't take long before they ran out of wood trying to get the steamboat free. The *A.B. Chambers* had lots of people and livestock on board, so they needed more wood to get going as fast as possible."

"Did they chop down some trees?" Doc guessed.

"No, apparently there was plenty of wood on flatboats up near a town called Commerce, not too far away, and the captain instructed Grant Marsh and Sam Clemens to take the yawl and some men and go to Commerce to get a flatboat loaded with wood. Sam skillfully guided the yawl through the ice-filled river, but then they ran into a *big* problem."

"More ice?" Mike guessed.

"Yup. A *huge* ice jam had formed ahead of them in a narrow place on the river, and it looked like it could break free anytime. They had to cross the river, but they knew the ice jam could break free any second, and then they'd be in *huge* trouble."

"Oh, no!" Jessie exclaimed. "It broke, didn't it?"

"Yes, it did. It broke as they were crossing, and it looked like it was all over for them. Grant Marsh assessed the situation and yelled, **'Turn back! We're going to get crushed!'** ... But Sam's instincts told him something much different. He held on to the rudder and ordered, **'No! Row as fast as you can!'"**

"Did they make it?" KT asked.

"Yes, just barely—they followed Sam's orders—but they looked back to where the boat would have ended up if they'd turned back when Grant Marsh wanted to. The river back there was a crazy, wild, boiling mass of floating ice chunks, and Grant Marsh knew that they all would have been killed if they'd done what he wanted to do. Sam Clemens had saved all their lives."

"Pretty amazing!" said Prez.

"It was," said Jack. "After that, Samuel Clemens and Grant Marsh kept in touch regularly, mostly with letters."

"How long did Mark Twain live?" asked Nick.

"That's a great story in itself," said Jack. "You've heard of Halley's Comet, right?"

"Sure," Kari replied, "that's that amazingly bright comet that appears every 75 years or so. I read where it was so bright in 1910, it was almost like a small sun, and you could easily see it in the daytime."

"When did it last appear?" asked Jessie.

"1986," said Egore.

"When is it coming back?" asked Kevin.

"July of 2061," Egore replied.

"Well, just imagine this," said Jack. "Samuel Clemens was born in 1835 when Halley's Comet was around, and he died of a heart attack *one day* after it appeared at its brightest the next time it appeared, 76 years later, in 1910. He even predicted he would die when Halley's Comet showed up again."

"No way!" said Kevin.

"That's what I thought," Jack said, chuckling. "But this is exactly what he said one year before he died, 'I came in with Halley's Comet in 1835. It is coming again next year, and I expect to go out with it. It will be the greatest disappointment of my life if I don't go out with Halley's Comet. The Almighty has said, no doubt, *Now here are these two unaccountable freaks. They came in together, they must go out together.*'"

"Wow!" Chad exclaimed.

"That was great story!" said Chad. "Thanks, Jack."

"A great story—told by one of the greatest football players of *all-time*," added Mike.

"Well, thanks," said Jack. "If I hang around you guys, I'm bound to get even smarter."

Everyone laughed.

Egore said, "I've been scanning Mark Twain's classic book *Life on the Mississippi* and it's pretty awesome."

"What did you find?" asked KT.

"Well, it's easy to tell that Mark Twain was a brilliant writer, and in the book, he makes it really clear that being a steamboatman was what every boy wanted to grow up to be. And being a pilot was the best job in the whole world at that time.

"Mark Twain also did a great job of describing what it was like being a steamboat pilot. He gives an excellent description of just how difficult and challenging the job could be. He put it this way. Imagine driving down the busiest street of the busiest city you've ever been in. In Mark Twain's case, that might have been New York City. Then imagine that you have to remember every detail of that block as you drive down that street—every sign, door, window, post, and sidewalk. You have to know this so well that you could be placed in any position on that street in the middle of a dark night, and you would be able to identify exactly where you were. Now, because the river changes constantly, imagine half the signs and other stuff on the streets are changed from month to month, and you still have to remember everything in perfect detail. Then, when you drive down the street the opposite way, it's a whole new challenge— just like when you go down the river, it's a whole different challenge than when you traveled up the river. That's what kind of memory and skill it takes to be a good steamboat pilot."

"Now I get it," said Chad. "Grant Marsh and Mark Twain must have had amazing memories to do all that."

"Yes, they did," said Egore. "And Grant Marsh used something else to help him out.

"What?" asked KT.

"He had a notebook near him in the pilot house where he wrote down all the important details he wanted to remember. For example, when he made the first ever trip by steamboat up the Yellowstone River, he wrote down names for the places he saw along the way, and many of those names are still used today."

"That's so cool," said Mike.

Prez said, "Troy and Jack, are you going to be able to go to St. Louis with us tomorrow morning?"

"I wouldn't miss it," said Jack.

"I'm so sorry," said Troy. "I've got some business to take care of tomorrow, so I won't be able to go along. I'll keep in touch with you, though, and I'll catch up with you later. I have a feeling this Grant Marsh adventure is going to continue for a while longer."

"Sounds great, but we'll miss you, Troy," said Jessie.

St. Louis Levee, 1852; *Author's collection*

CHAPTER 17

Apple Butter Stirring

As they approached the outskirts of St. Louis in the Exercise, they talked about what it was like when Grant Marsh first arrived there in 1852.

Prez said, "It's hard to even imagine how different St. Louis was back in the spring of 1852 when Grant Marsh came to St. Louis the first time. Remember, he was a deckhand on board the steamboat *Beaver* that operated between Pittsburgh and St. Louis—and he was still just a teenager."

Kevin added, "Back then, St. Louis was the third largest port in America after New York City and New Orleans, with 3,000 steamboats arriving there every year and the population was about 95,000 people."

Prez said, "Grant Marsh gets off the steamboat here in St. Louis, and what does he see almost immediately? A man with two babies. He finds out both parents had died of cholera, and the man was helping find someone to take care of the babies. There was a cholera epidemic in St. Louis at the time."

"What's cholera, Doc?" asked Nick.

"It's a very serious bacterial disease that causes dehydration and diarrhea—mostly spread through contaminated water. Cholera was a problem before they had water and sewage treatment plants and drinking water could become contaminated."

"Yikes," said Nick, grimacing.

"So his first impression of St. Louis wasn't good at all," said Chad. "Does anyone have a happier story from St. Louis?"

"KT and I do," said Kari.

"Go ahead." said Jack. "Please tell us."

"All right," said KT. "Turn the clock ahead about seven years from the time Grant Marsh first arrived in St. Louis. Grant Marsh would have been about 26 at the time. This is the romantic story of how he meets his future wife. I love this story."

"Does it involve kissing?" asked Mike.

"No," said Kari, "but it involves food—apple-butter to be specific."

"What's that?" asked Jessie.

Kari explained, "Picture a delicious sauce-like combination of apples with stuff like brown sugar, cinnamon, nutmeg, cloves, and ginger."

"Sounds good," said Kevin.

Egore said, "I'll gladly make some later, if you'd like."

"That would be great, Egore," said KT.

Kari continued, "So, there was this guy, let's call him *Chad* because we don't really know his real name—who worked on the steamboat with Grant Marsh."

"What did *Chad* do on the steamboat?" asked Chad, chuckling.

"He cleaned the privy," KT said with a straight face. Chad looked surprised.

KT giggled. "Actually, he was an engineer's apprentice or striker, so he had the really tough job of keeping the engine and boiler working."

Chad smiled. "Besides being tough, I'll bet Chad was a great guy."

"Oh, *pretty* great, I guess," said Kari. "Chad was also a real talker. While he was working on the steamboat, he would go on and on about this absolutely beautiful girl he was seeing in St. Louis. According to *Chad*, she was the most perfect girl in the whole wide world."

"And I wouldn't exaggerate about anything like *that*!" Chad said with authority. That was followed by lots of laughter from his friends.

"Yeah," said KT, "but the people on the boat got a little tired of hearing about this wonderful girl. Many of the men thought Chad was actually making her up. But Grant Marsh was kind to Chad, and he was also a good listener. He listened to Chad's stories, so Chad told him even more."

Chad smiled and said, "Grant Marsh had good taste. He liked Chad."

"Maybe," said Kari, "but even Grant Marsh wondered if this girl actually existed. He would laugh once in a while at Chad and question him about whether his story was true or not."

KT added, "But Chad insisted this girl existed, and he told Grant Marsh that he'd take him along to meet this girl when they got back to St. Louis."

"Did he?" asked Prez.

"Yes, he did," said KT. "It turns out the young lady,

who we all know was named *Katy*, was a real beauty."

"Of course, she was," said Chad, giggling.

Kari said, "Katy and her family had recently moved to St. Louis from Pennsylvania—the same state that Grant Marsh and Chad had moved from—and they had some customs and things in common because of that, including a custom called apple-butter stirring. So, when Katy knew Chad was bringing Grant Marsh over to her house, she invited some of her best friends to get together for an apple-butter stirring."

"How did that work?" asked Jack.

Kari said, "Picture a huge kettle with the apples and all that other good stuff I mentioned in it. It's cooking over a fire in the fireplace in a large room. When it's almost finished cooking, it gets pretty thick, and it needs lots of continuous stirring with a big heavy ladle, big enough so you can stand away from the fire and stir comfortably. This is also easier to do if two people are doing it together."

KT continued. "The young people are all sitting together in the room, dressed up nicely. Then a lady picks a partner to stir the apple-butter with her. After a while, another lady gets a turn at picking a partner to stir the apple-butter."

"That *is* romantic," said Jack.

"Did Grant Marsh get to stir the apple-butter with Katy?" Prez wanted to know.

"Not really," Kari replied. "First, I have to tell you that when Grant Marsh saw Katy, he was definitely a bit stunned and surprised. The girl Chad had talked about was just as beautiful as Chad said she was."

"I don't exaggerate about things like that!" Chad insisted.

KT said, "When Chad and Katy were stirring the apple-butter, Grant Marsh watched, and I think he got pretty jealous as their hands nearly touched on the big ladle."

"I think I could write a song about this," said Mike.

"I hope you do," said Egore.

"After watching some more," said Kari, "Grant Marsh did something that surprised himself—he walked over, very nervous, and whispered into Katy's ear, 'Maybe you and I can stir the apple-butter next time.' Katy turned and looked into his eyes. Then she smiled and said, 'All right.'"

"And … just a few months later … they were married," said KT.

"AWWWWWW!"

"But I'm a little worried about Chad and *his* feelings," said Chad.

Everyone got a good laugh out of that.

"I liked that story a lot," said Nick. "But how about a St. Louis story that's much less romantic."

"That would be a story like the Ice Gorge of 1856," said Prez. "Grant Marsh had another close call during this one."

"I like close-call stories," said Nick.

"Okay," Prez began. "Grant Marsh had only been in St. Louis about three years, and he wasn't even 22 years old yet. At the time, he was watchman on the *A.B. Chambers* during the winter. The river usually doesn't freeze over completely in St. Louis, but it did in 1856. It froze on New Year's Day and just got thicker after that. Grant Marsh said you could actually walk from steamboat to steamboat on the ice for about 20 blocks at that time.

"By late in February, it got warm in the upper rivers which caused the water to rise rapidly in St. Louis before the heavy ice had a chance to thaw. Then, on February 28, a *huge* avalanche of floating ice chunks came down the river causing major havoc—boats of all sorts were crushed and damaged. They were thrown around like little toy boats, they smashed into others, which smashed into more. This went on for two days, while people watched helplessly. There was absolutely nothing they could do about it, though, except get out of the way."

"What was it like for Grant Marsh?" asked Jessie.

"He must have had the scariest ride *imaginable*, through debris and wrecked boats, with huge piles of ice and ice chunks surrounding him. The *A.B. Chambers* was actually carried three miles from its starting point!"

"Unbelievable!"

"I definitely like apple-butter stirring story better," said Jessie.

CHAPTER 18

Fun in St. Louis

St. Louis was crowded with tens of thousands of happy people. Everyone was having a great time while they anxiously waited to see what was going to happen next.

All sorts of Grant Marsh merchandise was being sold on the streets of St. Louis. Sarabiskota and Jack Lambert picked out some awesome T-shirts and caps to wear. Several of the girls bought *Far West* necklaces.

In the morning, Jack Lambert and Sarabiskota went on a ride aboard the *Tom Sawyer* riverboat then they visited the Museum of Westward Expansion and the Old Courthouse. During the early afternoon, they went on tram ride to the top of the Gateway Arch, where they enjoyed wonderful views from the observation deck.

For dinner that evening, they were special guests of the mayor of St. Louis, Kimberly Kline, at Carmine's Steak House, near the Gateway Arch. They ate some of the greatest steaks they'd ever eaten in a private room in the restaurant.

While they were eating, Mayor Kline said, "I've been trying to keep up with everything regarding Grant Marsh that I possibly can, mostly by reading all your material on Spacebook. It seems that Captain Marsh moved up the steamboat ranks rapidly once he got here to St. Louis. How old was he when he finally made pilot and captain."

"It was 1866, and he was 32, I think," Doc answered.

"That's right," said Prez, "His first trip as captain and pilot was on board the *Luella*, and that trip took him from here in St. Louis all the way to Ft. Benton and back here."

"Did Grant and Katy Marsh start their family in St. Louis?" asked Mayor Kline.

"Yes," KT replied, "three kids were born here in St. Louis—John R., Grant C. and Carrie."

Mayor Kline said, "I seem to have read something about Grant Marsh serving in the Civil War during the time he and his family lived here. Do you know any more about that?"

"That's where Grant Marsh met General Ulysses S. Grant, who would later become our eighteenth president," said Egore. "Not long after Grant Marsh got married to Katy, the Civil War started on April 12, 1861, and Grant Marsh served in the Union's fleet of steamboats. His job was to help transport soldiers and supplies on the lower Mississippi River. At the Battle of Shiloh, he was the mate of the *John J. Roe*, one of the steamboats that transported the troops in General Grant's army. The steamboat was under fire during most of the first day's battle. Then, at night, Grant Marsh was busy helping get the troops across the river to the battlefield. Thanks to men like Grant Marsh on board those steamboats, fresh troops reinforced General Grant's exhausted forces and helped them win the battle."

"That's very interesting," said Mayor Kline. "I've noticed that, so far, whoever's leading us on this adventure seems to be following Grant Marsh's life chronologically— after Bismarck, that is. Grant Marsh was born in Pittsburgh area, and then he moved to St. Louis. If that chronological trend continues, where would we expect this adventure to take us next?"

"That would be Sioux City, Iowa," Prez answered. "The Grant Marsh family moved to Sioux City after St. Louis in 1870."

"Why Sioux City?" asked the mayor.

Egore explained, "Grant Marsh had to go where the steamboat business was, and most of his business was on the upper part the Missouri River at that time. The trade between St. Louis and the northwest was decreasing, and the railroad had gotten as far as Sioux City. That town then became the center for distribution of things to the Dakota Territory and Montana, where Grant Marsh was doing most of his work."

Suddenly, there was a big commotion in the restaurant. A man came over to their table. "Mayor! You've got to see this!"

CHAPTER 19

Teddy and Grant Marsh

Mayor Kline, Sarabiskota, and Jack Lambert rushed out of the restaurant and ran over to join the thousands of other people near the Gateway Arch. Approaching them from the west was a huge airplane, a really old airplane, all lit up in lights.

"Wow!" Mayor Kline exclaimed. "That's beautiful."

It was magnificent! As it slowly approached the Gateway Arch, Egore said, "This is phenomenal! The airplane is not really an airplane at all. It's a bunch of small lighted drones that must be programmed to form an airplane."

"Look!" someone yelled. "Two gigantic men just appeared—one riding on each wing!"

"Who are they?" someone else shouted.

"Wow! It's Teddy Roosevelt and Grant Marsh!" Prez shouted.

"Their plane looks like something the Wright Brothers might have flown!" Kevin exclaimed.

"Some of this makes sense," said Egore. "On October 11, 1910, Teddy Roosevelt was right here in St. Louis, and he became the first president to go for an airplane ride. But Grant Marsh was not on the plane with him. The pilot was a man by the name of Archie Hoxsey—and get this. Teddy and Hoxsey were actually flying on one of the Wright Brothers' planes, just like Kevin surmised. It wasn't the plane from their first flight on December 17, 1903, but a slightly more advanced one."

"Did he have fun?" asked KT.

"Oh, yes," Egore replied. "At first, Teddy turned down Hoxsey's invitation to fly but then he changed his mind. After he was done, he said it was the finest experience he had ever had. They took three steep dives during their short, four-minute flight. There's actually a film of him flying that day. I'll show it to you later."

"Do you think whoever's doing all this is trying to tell us Teddy and Grant Marsh were both in St. Louis that day?" asked Jack.

"Or maybe there's some other connection between the two that we don't know about," Mayor Kline suggested.

Egore said, "Grant Marsh wasn't living in St. Louis at the time, but he could have been visiting. He had lots of friends and family living here."

Suddenly, more lights, all-blue in color, appeared behind the plane, forming a beautiful banner trailing behind.

Ten seconds later, a message appeared on the banner in all-orange lights and it began flashing—**"Remember Grant Marsh!"**

The message changed—**"See You Tomorrow!"**

The message changed again.

"513!" Mayor Kline exclaimed. "I'll bet that's the clue to where this is all going next!"

***

JB and Madison looked at each other. "This is so much fun!" said Madison.

"It's crazy!" said JB excitedly. "Putting Grant Marsh and Teddy Roosevelt together on that plane was a great idea."

"Thanks," said Madison. "I'll bet everyone's going to have fun finding out how they're connected."

"I think that's a sure thing," JB said. "Now let's get going. We've got more work to do."

CHAPTER 20

A Steamboat Trip Like No Other

The *Exercise* was on the way to Yankton, South Dakota.

"That's pretty unbelievable!" exclaimed Jack Lambert. "Grant Marsh's house is still there in Yankton."

"Yes, at 513 Douglas Avenue," Doc answered referring to her phone. "I'm reading that Grant Marsh and his wife raised five children in that house, and it was plenty big for all of them. I guess the barn is still there too, and it's one of the only old barns still left in Yankton."

Jessie said, "And Grant Marsh really loved those ten years they lived in Yankton. He might have been spending most of his time on steamboats during the spring, summer, and early fall, but he had all winter to help raise his two sons and three daughters."

"The kids must have been going to school," said Jack, "because I see that two of Grant Marsh's sons, John and Grant C., finished their education in the Yankton schools."

"So, we know about the 513," Kari said, "but what about Teddy's connection to Grant Marsh? Did Teddy know Grant Marsh?"

Prez smiled. "I've been looking into that the past few hours, and I found some really fascinating stuff. They definitely knew each other, but I haven't found out where they actually met each other yet. It's interesting, because Teddy came to what would become North Dakota in 1883 to hunt buffalo. By that time, Grant Marsh had left the area because the railroads had taken most of the steamboats' business. Captain Marsh had moved to Memphis, Tennessee, where he could still find some work on steamboats.

"I actually found the copy of an old letter that involves both Captain Marsh and Teddy. The author of Captain Marsh's biography, Joseph Mills Hanson, wrote that letter to Captain Marsh in late February of 1909, just before the biography was published. Anyway, the letter referred to how great it would be if they could get Teddy to come to North Dakota for a hunting trip with them, because it would be a great way to help get publicity for their new book. The letter mentions the fact that Teddy wouldn't be able to do it because he had just completed his second term as president of the United States, and he was on an African safari at the time.

"And then I found something else that's hard to believe. Teddy has a pretty incredible connection to steamboats. *Another Roosevelt*, Teddy's great-granduncle Nicholas Jacobus Roosevelt, designed and built the *first* steamboat to travel on the western waters of the United States. His trip actually opened up steamboat travel on the western rivers."

"No way!" said Nick. "This just keeps getting more and more interesting."

"Yes, it does," said Prez. "The steamboat was called *the New Orleans*, and this all happened in 1811, 23 years before Grant Marsh was even born—47 years before Teddy was born. Nicholas actually traveled on the steamboat from Pittsburgh to New Orleans—about 2,000 miles in 12 weeks—and what an amazing trip it turned out to be!"

FIRST BOAT BUILT ON THE WESTERN WATERS, 1812.

THE NEW ORLEANS; *AUTHOR'S COLLECTION*

"I think I would have liked **Nick**-olas," said Nick, giggling. "But what was so amazing about the trip?"

Prez said, "Let me just say it was 12 weeks and about 2,000 miles through mostly wilderness country with lots of unexpected surprises."

"What kind of surprises?" asked KT.

"I'll try to give you the highlights," said Prez. "They

started out on October 20, 1911. Many people criticized Nicholas for taking his pregnant wife, Lydia, along, plus their two-year-old daughter."

"Why?" Kari asked.

"Remember, they would be traveling through mostly wilderness, with lots of danger. By the way, they took their big Newfoundland dog, Tiger, along too, and he gets involved in this story later. ... So, ten days after they left Pittsburgh, they get as far as Louisville, Kentucky, and Lydia has a baby boy, who they name Henry Latrobe."

Egore said, "Prez, we should mention here that baby Henry Latrobe was actually named after Lydia's father, Benjamin Henry Latrobe, who was the architect of the United States Capitol."

"No way!" said Nick.

"More incredible history," said Prez. "So, they stayed in Louisville and gave Lydia a chance to recover and the river a chance to rise so they can get over the rapids and the falls there. During that time, Nicholas had time to take passengers on short trips up and down the river. Also, they got a chance to view an awesome sight in the sky."

"What?" asked Mike.

"A comet. It must have been unbelievably bright too, with the head of the comet even bigger than the sun. It was called the Great Comet of 1811. It could be seen with the naked eye for 260 days, but it was its absolute brightest at this particular time. ... It might have been a bad omen for what was about to come."

"Oh, no!" said Doc. "Not a bad omen!"

"Was Tiger involved at all?" asked Chad, anxious to hear what happened next.

"Yes, he was," Prez answered. "They took off from

Louisville, and on December 16, the steamboat was anchored near Owensboro, Kentucky, about 200 miles east of New Madrid, Missouri. They didn't know it, but something *really* amazing was about to happen the next day. Tiger was the only one on board the *New Orleans* who sensed that something bad was going to happen. That night, for the first time, he didn't want to sleep on the deck as he usually did. Instead, he insisted on sleeping in the cabin."

"Did a tornado hit?" Kari guessed.

"A meteor?" Kevin tried.

"A sharknado!?" Nick said, laughing.

"Maybe even worse than a sharknado," said Prez. "They didn't know it, but they were headed straight toward the epicenter of the greatest earthquake in American history."

"No way!" Jessie exclaimed.

"Yes, way," Prez replied. "There were falling trees, riverbanks collapsing, disappearing islands, tons of floating debris, and towns almost completely destroyed. This earthquake was *huge* and actually changed the course of the river so much that the pilot of the *New Orleans* got lost at one point. Many of the landmarks that he would have recognized were gone."

"Unbelievable!" said Doc.

"It really was," said Prez. "Many American Indians and others along the river actually blamed the steamboat *New Orleans* for the earthquake and all the tremors that followed. They thought the comet had something to do with it too. At one point a large canoe of Chickasaw Indians tried to catch up with the steamboat, but eventually the *New Orleans* was able to outrun it."

"Did the *New Orleans* make it?" asked KT, looking scared.

"It did, but they even had a small fire to put out in the cabin. On December 19, they got to New Madrid, but that town was destroyed. They couldn't even stop and pick up survivors because they knew they would be overrun if they did. They were also freaked out because they hadn't even seen another boat on the river in three days."

"So," said Jack with a sigh, "we've got the rapids, the birth of a baby boy, a fire, and the biggest earthquake ever in America. I guess they didn't have any fun, did they?"

Prez chuckled. "I guess there was a little fun on December 30 when they got as far as Natchez, Mississippi, and there was a wedding on board the steamboat—the very *first* wedding on a steamboat. An engineer got married to Lydia's maid. ... They finally got to New Orleans on January 10, 1812."

"What a trip!" Jack exclaimed. "I can't believe I never heard about it before."

Chapter 21

Lonesome Charlie and Yellowstone Kelly

"Prez," said Jessie, "I know I'm not the only one who's feeling more and more like someone is doing this Grant Marsh stuff primarily to get your attention."

"I agree," said Kevin. "After that Teddy on the airplane with Grant Marsh thing, I'm almost positive."

"Me, too," said KT. "But it's really hard to imagine someone doing all of this just for *you*."

Everyone laughed except Prez. He was dumbfounded by what this all meant.

Doc said, "It also looks like whoever is doing this has broken that chronological pattern, too."

Egore suggested, "Maybe they just skipped Sioux City because Grant Marsh and his family didn't live there very long before they moved to Yankton. Sioux City is barely mentioned in his biography."

"Why did Grant Marsh move to Yankton anyway?" Kari asked.

Prez explained, "He actually moved there during the summer of 1873. By that time, the Northern Pacific Railroad had tracks between Bismarck and Fargo, and lots of settlers followed the railroad. The settlers needed lots of stuff, and steamboats were a great way to get that stuff there. In 1871, Grant Marsh became a founding partner of a big company that had seven steamboats that took people and materials around the upper Missouri River area. Yankton had become an important port by that time, so that's where those steamboats took off from."

"What were Bismarck and Mandan like then?" asked Mike.

"Remember," said Prez, "this was four years before the *Far West* brought those wounded back to Ft. Abraham Lincoln. Mandan didn't exist yet, but Ft. McKeen was built in 1872 just south of where Mandan would sprout up, and the name of the fort would be changed to Ft. Abraham Lincoln less than a year later, the same year Custer arrived. Bismarck was already getting pretty big—it was called Edwinton in 1872, then it became Bismarck one year later. By 1874, it had about 1,200 people, which included 18 saloons and eight pool halls and one bowling alley. It was a really rough, dangerous town."

"And Yankton was the capital of the Dakota Territory in 1872, right?" asked Chad.

"That's right," said Prez. "Yankton became the capital of the Dakota Territory in 1861, when Abraham Lincoln was president. It was the capital until 1883, when Bismarck took over. By the way, the Dakota Territory covered much more than just present-day

North and South Dakota, but there were many more Native Americans in the territory than U.S. citizens. When Yankton became capital in 1861, it had a population of only about 300, and there were about the same number in Pembina, plus there were some small settlements along the Missouri River. It was definitely a sparsely populated territory."

Jack asked, "Did anything special happen during the time Grant Marsh lived in Yankton?"

"Lots of things happened," said Prez. "Grant Marsh said it was the happiest time in his life. Besides helping raise his young family, his job must have been really exciting and challenging. He took his steamboats to places that only the American Indians had seen before. It's interesting—during those ten years he lived in Yankton, he actually spent most of his time a long way from there, between Bismarck and the Yellowstone River Valley. He also worked with some amazing people during that time."

"Like who?" asked Nick.

"Like Lonesome Charlie Reynolds," said Prez. "Charlie was the best hunter and guide in the Dakota Territory, and Grant Marsh and Charlie became really good friends."

"How did he get the name Lonesome Charlie?" asked Chad.

"After he fought for the Union in the Civil War, he basically drifted from state to state and kept to himself pretty much."

"Please tell us more, Prez," said Jack.

"Sure," said Prez. "Charles Alexander Reynolds came from a good family in the East. His dad was a doctor and they moved to Kansas when Charlie was in his teens. He went to college for three years there, but then he joined the Union Army when the Civil War started. After the Civil War, Charlie started drifting from place to place and job to job until he ended up in what is now North Dakota.

"Charlie was an unbelievable hunter, and he was hired by the U.S. Army to supply fresh meat for Ft. Stevenson and Ft. Rice and that's where Captain Marsh met him. The captain liked to tell people the story that gives you an idea of just what a great hunter Lonesome Charlie was—it goes something like this.

"Charlie's amazing hunting skills were well-known, and there was a term that some of the other hunters used to describe it—*Reynold's Luck*. Many of the members of the Mandan, Gros Ventre, and Arikara tribes at Fort Berthold actually thought he had some type of magic, and Charlie's life was actually in danger there because of it.

"One time, in the middle of the winter, when meat was getting scarce, Lonesome Charlie went hunting with a young half-breed Arikara Indian named Peter Beauchamp. Charlie and Peter ended up going down to the Little Missouri River area in a wagon to hunt, and not long after they got there, they saw eight elk. Well, with his unbelievable skill, Charlie was able to shoot all eight elk with his trusty rifle.

"When they got back to Ft. Berthold, the Gros Ventre Indians couldn't believe it when they saw the wagon pull in, loaded with all the elk! They'd hunted that place recently and had no luck at all. Peter Beauchamp just made it worse when he made up a story explaining

Charlie's luck to the Gros Ventre Indians. Peter told them that Lonesome Charlie had a special medicine he hid in a secret pocket in a small black bottle, and he sprinkled a few drops of it on the trail. After that, all he did was wait till the elk came down the trail and then he shot them."

"Oh no!" exclaimed KT. "Now those Indians must *really* get mad!"

"That's right. They believed the fake story, and it was more than they could stand. Two hundred of them rushed to the store where Charlie was resting, and they threatened to kill him if he didn't give them the bottle with the magic liquid in it. Lonesome Charlie told them he didn't have any bottle—then the Gros Ventre Indians went out and threatened to kill Charlie's horses. Well, Lonesome Charlie followed them outside, pointed his rifle at them and said, 'The first man to touch one of these horses is going to die! ... The Gros Ventres backed down. After that, Charlie gave two of the elk to the Arikara tribesmen, who hadn't threatened him. But Charlie didn't give any elk to the Gros Ventres.

"Lonesome Charlie became a close friend with Grant Marsh over the years. Charlie met Custer in 1869, and when the Seventh Cavalry came to Ft. Abraham Lincoln in 1873, Lonesome Charlie was a guide for them. In 1875, Grant Marsh wanted Charlie to go with them as a guide and hunter on an incredible expedition to the find the headwaters of the Yellowstone River on the steamboat *Josephine* and they had an adventure that was incredible. On that trip, Grant Marsh even named an island after Lonesome Charlie called *Reynold's Island*.

"The next summer, Lonesome Charlie died with

Custer. Charlie was actually on the *Far West* with Grant Marsh before he left for the Little Big Horn, and he wasn't feeling very good. I guess he had a felon on his hand. What exactly is a felon, Doc?"

"It's a painful abscess caused by bacterial infection," Doc answered.

"Thanks," said Prez. "Dr. Porter was treating Lonesome Charlie for the felon at the time. Despite all of Captain Marsh's efforts at trying to get Charlie to stay on board the boat, he wouldn't have anything to do with it. He'd been preparing for the campaign for two years, and he was determined to be part of it."

"So sad," said Kevin.

Prez said, "There are some stories about Lonesome Charlie having some premonitions about what was going to happen to him the next day, but some think it had something to do with his medical condition. Anyway, the night before, Charlie gave away many of his personal items to soldiers. Then, the next day, as they were riding toward the Indian village where the battle would take place, he asked the interpreter, Fred Gerard, for some whiskey. It was weird—because Charlie never drank.

"Lonesome Charlie died heroically. Dr. Porter was helping a wounded soldier in a clump of bushes when Charlie noticed that some of the Indians were trying to shoot the doctor. Lonesome Charlie yelled at the doctor to warn him and then he got shot and died."

"That's so sad," said KT.

"I like Lonesome Charlie," Jessie added.

"Tell us about another friend of Grant Marsh's," said Chad.

"Okay. There was another good friend of Grant

Marsh who had a lot in common with Lonesome Charlie. This man was also a great guide and hunter. His name was Yellowstone Kelly. Just look at his photo."

YELLOWSTONE KELLY, *AUTHOR'S COLLECTION*

"He could have been a movie star," said Doc.

"His story was actually made into a movie in 1959, and it's no wonder," said Prez. "What an exciting life he had! Yellowstone Kelly grew up in New York State. His real name was Luther S. Kelly, and he got a good education, and his family was pretty well off. Luther loved reading books about the Wild West which were quite common back then. He dreamed of going there one day, living a life of adventure, and fighting American Indians, just like in the books he was reading.

"Well, Kelly didn't just read about it, he actually left his comfortable home when he was still only in his teens. Then he made the long, difficult trip, eventually ending up in Ft. Stevenson. There he was, in a very dangerous place by himself—a place where hostile Sioux Indians were likely to kill anyone outside of their tribe if they dared leave the fort. ... At first, no one at Ft. Stevenson took Luther very seriously. They gave him a really rough time, made fun of him, and nicknamed him *The Kid*. Kelly was pretty amazing, because he took all their teasing without getting upset and just waited for his chance to prove himself."

"I like this guy a lot," said Chad. "Does he get a chance to prove himself?"

"He does," said Prez. "Grant Marsh liked to tell the story about how he accomplished that. You see, at the time, no one would dare travel between Ft. Stevenson and Ft. Buford without a troop escort. Once a month, a whole company of troops, at least 100 soldiers, would escort the mail between the two forts. But there was this one time after Kelly arrived at the fort, there were no troops available for the mail run. That's when Luther Kelly saw his chance to prove himself. He volunteered to make the mail run *by himself*. At first, the commanding officer laughed it off, but Kelly insisted. All the American Indians and other people in the fort predicted Luther wouldn't get a mile before he would be killed. They knew how dangerous it was. So, Kelly took off. A few hours later, he arrived at Ft. Berthold, 18 miles away, unharmed. The people at the fort thought it was a bit of a miracle. The rest of the trip to Ft. Buford was supposed to be even more dangerous. He hadn't gone too far, when he came to a steep coulee that led into a big valley. There, he was attacked by two Sioux warriors, one with a gun and one with bow and arrow."

"What happened?" asked Nick anxiously.

"Kelly killed them both, and he got an arrow wound above his right knee during the fight. The American Indians at the fort that were enemies of the Sioux were totally amazed when they found out about it. They called Kelly *The Little Man with a Strong Heart.*"

"Did he make it all the way to Ft. Buford after that?" asked Kevin.

"Yes," answered Prez, "not only that, but he got the contract for carrying the mail for the rest of the year. Then, he got tired of that and set out for the Yellowstone Valley and became quite famous. Captain Marsh got to know Yellowstone Kelly really well when he captained the *Key West* exploring the Yellowstone Valley in 1873. Yellowstone Kelly was hired to be the guide, and he turned out to be a great scout and hunter. He also became a really good friend of Captain Marsh as the *Key West* went where no riverboat had ever gone before. Kelly's gun, which he called *Old Sweetness*, helped him get all the fresh meat they needed on that journey."

"Whatever happened to Yellowstone Kelly?" asked Doc.

"He lived an amazing, long life of adventure. He went on an Alaskan Expedition, he fought in the Spanish-American War, and he became a good friend to Teddy Roosevelt, who he met while Teddy lived in North Dakota. Yellowstone Kelly was part of Teddy's Tennis Cabinet, a group of Teddy's closest friends and advisors. He was there at a farewell luncheon at the end of Teddy's presidency in 1909. Yellowstone Kelly died at the age of 79, and you won't believe where he's buried."

"Where?" asked Jack.

"He's buried on *Kelly* Mountain overlooking the *Yellowstone* River near Billings, Montana."

"Talk about the perfect burial place for a guy named Yellowstone Kelly," said Mike.

Chapter 22

A Swimmer and Sitting Bull

Jessie said, "Kari and I came across two things that happened during Grant Marsh's last few years living in Yankton that were pretty cool. One involves something unusual in the river, and I'll start with that one."

"Was it a pirate ship?" Nick guessed.

"A huge rubber ducky?" KT tried.

"A yellow submarine?" Mike guessed. Immediately he started singing the famous Beatles song "Yellow Submarine" and soon, Jack and his Sarabiskota friends *really* got into the music. Doc was the first to get up and start dancing. It wasn't long before everyone joined her. Prez was even enjoying himself, but Egore seemed to be having the best time of everyone—and the best dancing moves.

When the song was over, they all laughed and applauded. Jack said, "That was awesome!"

"Egore, I never knew you could dance like that!"

Doc exclaimed. "You were amazing!"

"Well, thanks," said Egore, smiling and blushing. "That was fun!"

"We've got to do this more often," said Prez. "But now, Jessie, please get back to your story. What was in the river?"

"It might have been crazier than a yellow submarine," said Jessie. It was the summer of 1881 and Grant Marsh was in charge of the steamboat *Eclipse*. They were leaving Ft. Berthold when everyone noticed something coming down the river toward them that they couldn't identify. As it got closer, they realized what it was—it was a man swimming—but this wasn't just any ordinary man swimming casually in any ordinary swimming suit. It was a man named Paul Boyton, swimming on his back in a crazy-looking rubber suit, holding onto a small, two-bladed paddle to help him move through the water. He was even towing a small boat behind him called the *Baby Mine* that had some food and other provisions in it. I've got a few photos of Paul Boyton to show you that will give you a good idea what they saw that day."

PAUL BOYTON; *AUTHOR'S COLLECTION*

152

PAUL BOYTON; *AUTHOR'S COLLECTION*

"Unbelievable! Way back then?" said Prez.

"As a swimmer myself, I can't believe he was swimming all the way from Glendive, Montana, to St. Louis," said Jessie. "The American Indians at Ft. Berthold watched for a while and were completely confused and dumbfounded. Many of them ran to their camps and told their people about a big beaver with two tails coming down the river."

"Too funny!" said Mike, laughing.

Doc asked, "Did you find out anything more about Boyton?"

"Yes," Jessie replied. "The guy did a bunch of incredible things in his life. He's actually in the

International Swimming Hall of Fame. He did many long-distance swims, like swimming the English Channel in 24 hours in 1875. He developed a rubber suit that was designed to save steamboat passengers. It had air pockets in it that could be inflated using tubes. It was a lot like modern-day wetsuits, and that's the thing he wore when Grant Marsh saw him on the Missouri River. Boyton also did an aquatic circus act in the Barnum Circus, and he even opened the first amusement park to charge admission—called Paul Boyton's Water Chutes in Chicago. I've got a photo of it."

PAUL BOYTON'S WATER CHUTES; *LIBRARY OF CONGRESS*

"It looks like a cool waterpark," said Nick.

"He really *was* ahead of his time," said Egore.

Kari said, "My story involves one of the leaders of the Lakota Sioux that defeated Custer at the Little Big Horn."

"Sitting Bull?" Kevin guessed.

"That's right," said Kari. "After the Little Big Horn, Sitting Bull had gone to Canada where he had held out with some of his people until the summer of 1881, but they were barely surviving there. That summer, Sitting Bull and 187 women, men, and children came to Ft. Buford and gave themselves up. Then they were taken to Ft. Randall which was on the Missouri River northwest of Yankton.

SITTING BULL, 1883; *AUTHOR'S COLLECTION*

"Then, in the spring of 1882, which was six years after Custer was killed at the Little Big Horn, Grant Marsh was hired to take Sitting Bull and his people to Ft. Yates to live. Grant Marsh had purchased the steamboat *W.J. Behan* recently, so he transported them on his new steamboat. Sitting Bull and his two wives and children were on board.

"By this time, Sitting Bull was quite a celebrity, and he took advantage of it. As they traveled along the river and made stops along the way, he charged one dollar for his autograph. A missionary priest in Canada had taught Sitting Bull how to write his name, but he wrote S-E-i-t-t-i-n-g Bull instead of S-i-t-t-i-n-g Bull, which people thought was pretty cool. When they got to Chamberlain and Pierre, there were so many people waiting to get autographs that it was hard to keep the huge crowds in control.

"Grant Marsh mentioned something that was really peculiar about the Lakota Indians that he noticed while they were on his steamboat. For some strange reason, they couldn't walk up the stairs. They had to go up on their hands and knees."

"Huh?" said Chad.

"There wasn't any explanation for it," said Kari. "Grant Marsh also said that Sitting Bull didn't speak English at the time. But through an interpreter, he let Captain Marsh know that he wanted his carved pipestem. A pipestem is the handle on the pipe, and Grant Marsh's was a beautifully carved wooden one that Marsh had been given earlier on the trip by a man named Fran Chadron. Grant Marsh refused to sell it, but Sitting Bull was very persistent. Finally, Captain Marsh offered it to Sitting Bull for 50 dollars. He had the interpreter tell Sitting Bull something like, 'You scared the heck out me for 20 years. You should give me *something* for that.' Sitting Bull replied, 'I did not come on *your* land to scare you. If you had not come on *mine*, you would not have been scared either.'"

"Unreal," said Nick.

"Why did the Captain Marsh and his family leave Yankton?" asked Jack.

Prez explained, "The railroad kept expanding, and that became the best way to move people and animals and stuff around the area, so Grant Marsh had to find work someplace where he could still work on steamboats. But you're not going to believe what happened to Yankton in March of 1881 that also had some effect on the town's importance as a steamboat port. It reminded me of what happened in St. Louis in 1856."

"Ice Gorge!" six people said at the same time.

"You're way too smart," said Prez. "There was an awful winter with lots of snow and ice in that part of the country, and the ice upstream began to melt before the ice downstream. On March 27, there was an ice jam on the Missouri River and it suddenly burst. Huge blocks of ice and lots of water flowed toward Yankton. This photo gives you an idea of what that all did.

YANKTON ICE JAM, 1881: *AUTHOR'S COLLECTION*

"Yikes!" said Jack.

"Two steamboats and the ferry were destroyed and many other boats were damaged. An area across the river from Yankton on the other side of the river called Green Island was pretty much wiped out. Their church was carried right off its foundation and carried down the river, with its bell still ringing."

"Incredible!" Kevin exclaimed.

"Where did Grant Marsh go after he left Yankton?" asked KT.

"Memphis, Tennessee," said Prez.

Mike looked shocked, then he started speaking in his Elvis Presley voice. "Do you mean we might be going to the home of Elvis Presley after Yankton? Thank you. Thank you very much!"

Then Mike started singing the song "Memphis Tennessee" with his wonderful Elvis voice. ... "Long distance information, give me Memphis, Tennessee ...

Chapter 23

Fun Times in Yankton

The *Exercise* landed at the Sioux Falls Airport. From there, Jack Lambert and Sarabiskota flew on board the *Flying Teddy* toward Yankton, about 60 miles away. After the short flight, they landed in the Lewis and Clark Recreation Area, just six miles west of Yankton.

Mike Kern, the mayor of Yankton, along with his wife, Joletta, and their 14-year-old daughter, Katrice, were there to greet them when they landed. After friendly greetings and introductions, the mayor said, "Sarabiskota! Jack Lambert! I can't thank you enough for coming here. This whole Grant Marsh adventure is the biggest and best thing to happen to Yankton in a long time—and you're all such an important part of it."

"It's so nice of you to say that," said Kari.

Prez added, "We're just glad to be able to witness all this close-up and share it with the rest of the world."

Joletta Kern walked over to Jack. "And I have to tell

you something, Jack Lambert. My family is loaded with a bunch of Green Bay Packers fans, but we still think *you* are one of the greatest football players of all-time."

"Thanks so much," said Jack with a big smile. "I want you to know that I always liked playing football in Green Bay. The whole game atmosphere in your stadium was fantastic—and the fans were *great*."

Joletta said, "And Mike, my daughter might be too shy to tell you this, but she's one of your biggest fans—and so am I. I hope you're performing in the park this afternoon."

Mike said, "Thank you, Joletta and Katrice. Yes, I plan on singing in your park. In fact, I have a new song I'm writing that I'm going to introduce."

"I can't wait!" said Katrice, blushing.

"Now, I've got a suggestion," said Mayor Kern. "Actually, it was Joletta and Katrice's suggestion. We've got our big camper over there—with plenty of room for all of us. We thought maybe we could head up the road a few miles to the marina and take our pontoon out on Lewis and Clark Lake for a short cruise before we head into town."

"Awesome!" said Kevin.

"Perfect," Chad added.

"How big is the lake?" asked Mike.

"It's about 30 miles long," Mayor Kern answered. "It's loaded with largemouth and smallmouth bass too. If any of you want to put a fishing pole in the water, I'll get you fishing licenses. You just might catch something."

"That would be awesome!" said Kevin.

"Thanks," said Nick.

"Oh, it's our pleasure," said Mayor Kern.

While they were cruising on Lewis and Clark Lake, Mayor Kern said, "This whole area was already filling up with people last night, and everything seems to be going really well so far. After what took place in Bismarck and Pittsburgh and St. Louis, I think everyone's expecting something really big to happen here tonight."

"I think that's inevitable," said Egore.

"We can't wait!" said Jessie.

"What are the names of that dam and those beautiful orangish-white cliffs over there?" asked Doc.

"The dam is the Gavins Point Dam, and the cliffs there are the Calumet Bluffs," answered Katrice. "We learned in school that Lewis and Clark had a meeting with the Yankton Sioux over there in early August of 1804."

"What a beautiful meeting place," said KT.

"I've hiked over there," said Katrice. "The bluffs look a lot like chalk, and the clay that they're made of is just as hard as chalk, too."

Photo courtesy of Paul Harens

***

No one caught a fish, but no one got too serious about fishing either. Both the conversation and the view from the boat were exceptional.

After they left the Lewis and Clark Recreation Area, Mayor Kern said, "We'll make a few stops in town before it gets too crazy and busy, and then I'll buy you all breakfast."

Their first stop was the Dakota Territorial Museum. There, they got a chance to see the original model of the *Far West*, the one that was used when they built the steamboat in Pittsburgh.

Far West MODEL; *AUTHOR PHOTO*

Their next stop was the Grant Marsh house at 513 Douglas Avenue.

Mayor Kern explained, "From reading all your

material on Spacebook, I think you all already know that Grant Marsh bought this house in 1877, and now the church next door is using it mostly as an office and for some school rooms. They're using the barn for storage."

"It's just incredible to imagine that Grant Marsh used to live in this house with his family."

"The house has been kept in really good shape."

GRANT MARSH HOME; *AUTHOR PHOTOS*

After leaving the Marsh home, they went down to the riverfront area and walked on the Meridian Bridge.

Mayor Kern explained, "The Meridian Highway Bridge was dedicated in 1924, which would be about eight years after Grant Marsh died."

"How did it get that name?" asked Doc.

Grant Marsh Home; *Author photos*

INSIDE THE GRANT MARSH HOME; *PHOTOS COURTESY OF CAROL SMITH*

"The Meridian Highway was an early highway from Winnipeg to Mexico City, which ran along the Sixth Principal Meridian, which you might remember from your studies of latitude and longitude. It was originally a toll bridge, built with mostly local money. In 1983, the lift span stopped being movable, so they took out the machinery and the operator's house. When that new bridge north of the Meridian Bridge called the Discovery Bridge was opened in 2009, the Meridian Bridge was closed, but then they reopened it for people to use for walking, biking, and hiking in 2011."

MERIDIAN HIGHWAY BRIDGE; *AUTHOR PHOTO*

"Why does it have two decks?" asked Chad.

"They originally thought the lower deck would be for the railroad line going north and south, but that never happened. By the 1920s, the boom times for railroad construction were over."

"What's the deal with all the locks on there?" Nick asked.

Joletta said, "I guess this type of thing has been going on for a long time in Europe. Basically, couples buy padlocks, write their names or initials on them, padlock them to the bridge, then throw the keys into the water."

Locks on the Meridian Highway Bridge; *Photo courtesy of Jennifer O'Donley*

"How did that get started?" asked Jack.

"We talked about that in school," said Katrice. "It started because of a romantic story that comes from a Serbian town sometime in the early 1900s. There was a school teacher named Nada who was in love with a soldier, but then sadly, the soldier had to go to war. While he was off fighting, he ended up marrying another woman he met during the war, and he never came back to Nada. She ended up dying alone, brokenhearted. A poet wrote about it, and the young girls started placing locks on a bridge in their town—now called the Bridge of Love—as symbols of their love. They thought doing that would prevent them from the same fate as Nada."

"Thanks, Katrice," said Jack. "You did a great job telling us that story."

"You're welcome," Katrice replied.

After they left the bridge, they walked nearby, where the Dakota Territory Capitol replica stood, right next to the statue of Captain Grant Marsh.

DAKOTA TERRITORY CAPITOL REPLICA: *AUTHOR PHOTO*

Mayor Kern said, "The real Capitol Building was built in 1862, and it was sold and dismantled way back in 1886. It was at the corner of 4th and Capitol Street, and, of course, it was there during the time Grant Marsh was living in Yankton. You'll recall, Yankton was the capital of the Dakota Territory from 1861 until April 1883, when Bismarck became the capital."

After that, they only had to walk a few feet to get to the life-sized statue of Captain Grant Marsh. Mayor Kern said, "This statue was sculpted back in 1989 by a man named Frank Yaggie. ... I've got a suggestion. Let's ask someone to take a group photo of us here by the statue, then I'll take you all to my favorite restaurant for breakfast. We'll come back here to the park this afternoon after I show you around town."

GRANT MARSH STATUE; *AUTHOR'S PHOTO*

"Sounds like a great plan," said Kari.

"I hope you have lots of money," said Nick. "I'm hungry."

"No problem," said Mayor Kern, laughing.

As they were having their group photo taken, many

people in the area recognized Sarabiskota, Jack Lambert, and the mayor and his family. Many of them walked over and asked if they could take photos of everyone, and that's what took place the next 25 minutes.

GRANT MARSH STATUE, DAKOTA TERRITORY CAPITOL REPLICA, AND THE MERIDIAN HIGHWAY BRIDGE; *AUTHOR'S PHOTO*

***

Riverside Park was the place to be that afternoon and evening. There were thousands of excited, happy people and plenty of activities and food and entertainment. Everyone was anticipating when something related to Grant Marsh was going to happen—and what that was going to be.

Later, as darkness was setting in, Mike was performing on stage in the park. He had just finished singing his third Elvis song, "Heartbreak Hotel", and the crowd cheered and screamed. JB and Madison were cheering and screaming too, standing near the front of the stage, just a few feet from Sarabiskota, Jack Lambert, Mayor Kern, and his family.

When the cheering had stopped, Mike said, "Thank you! Thank you very much! I'm writing a special song to salute this journey we've all been on these past few days, following the story of the greatest steamboatman in history—Captain Grant Prince Marsh! I'm not quite finished with it yet, but the chorus goes something like this."

Mike began singing in his beautiful Elvis voice:

Now we know there's really no mys-tery,
Grant Marsh is the greatest steamboatman in his-tory!
But we've still got a mighty big mys-tery.
Who's got us learning all this Grant Marsh his-tory?
And I'd really *really* like to know for sure,
Where are we headed *next* on this his-tory tour?

There was huge applause when Mike was finished. JB reached into her pocket and pushed a button on a small device.

Soon, a little girl pointed into the air at something approaching them from down the river, all lit up in lights. "It's Superman!" she called out.

"No, it's Captain Grant Marsh!" someone else shouted.

Then someone else pointed the opposite direction. "What's that coming up the river?"

"It's the *Far West*!"

Everyone watched for the next several seconds, totally transfixed. Captain Grant Marsh eventually flew above the Meridian Bridge then landed feet-first on top of the middle span.

"AHHHHHHH!" the crowd reacted then they cheered.

Ten seconds later, the *Far West* flew into the air and landed next to Grant Marsh on top of the bridge.

Everyone cheered and cheered.

A deep voice came from the Grant Marsh statue on the bridge. "I hope all of you have enjoyed learning all about me and my life so far. Where am I going next? Watch the fireworks display to find out!"

For the next 15 minutes, a huge, spectacular fireworks display came from the Meridian Bridge. Then there was a pause for about five seconds. … A rocket went high into the air and exploded.

"**Mandan!**" the crowd yelled as it was spelled out in the air in beautiful red letters.

A second rocket went up high in the air and exploded.

"**Moustache!**" the crowd yelled as it was spelled out in the air in beautiful white letters.

A third rocket went up in the air and exploded.

"**Mandan!**" it spelled out in beautiful blue letters.

"Mandan Moustache Mandan!?" Nick said, confused.

"Huh!?" said KT.

JB and Madison giggled. "It shouldn't take them long to figure this one out," said JB.

Chapter 24

Mandan Moustache Mandan

The fireworks ended, and people all over the world immediately tried to solve the *Mandan Moustache Mandan* clue. The people living in Mandan, North Dakota, were especially excited to have their town name appearing in the clue twice, but most of them suspected right away that Mandan was not going to be the next stop for the Grant Marsh adventure.

Twelve-year-old Paulette Bullinger was trying to solve the clue with two of her friends in Huff, North Dakota. She loved history and she loved reading mysteries, so this whole Grant Marsh adventure was really fun for her.

Less than 20 minutes later, she was pretty sure she'd figured out where the adventure was headed. She started explaining it to her friends, "The moustache clue refers to a lady who lived in Ft. Benton who they called Madame Moustache. She was a real character. Her real name was Simone Jules, then she went by the name Eleanor Dumont,

MADAME MOUSTACHE; *AUTHOR'S COLLECTION*

but she was known as Madame Moustache for obvious reasons. Look at her photo."

"Oh, wow!" one of her friends exclaimed. "That's a pretty good moustache."

At the same time, Sarabiskota, Jack Lambert, and the Kerns were inside the Kerns' camper—also talking about Madame Moustache.

Kari said, "She was quite a character—but one particular event made her a real hero in Ft. Benton. In early June of 1867, the steamer *Deer Lodge* got to Ft.

Benton, and the passengers on board spread the word that the *Walter B. Dance* was right behind them, and someone on the ship had smallpox."

THE STEAMBOAT *DEER LODGE; OVERHOLSER HISTORICAL RESEARCH CENTER, FORT BENTON, MT*

THE *WALTER B. DANCE; OVERHOLSER HISTORICAL RESEARCH CENTER, FORT BENTON, MT*

"What's smallpox, Doc?" asked Nick.

"It was highly contagious disease that was eradicated in 1980 through a worldwide immunization program, but it caused many many people around the world to die before then because it was so contagious and deadly. It involved severe flu-like symptoms followed by some really uncomfortable red spots with blisters and then scars."

"Gruesome," said KT.

Kari continued telling the story. "So Madame Moustache carried two pistols, ran down to the levee where the *Walter B. Dance* had just arrived, and fired her pistol into the pilot house window of the steamboat. The steamer left, and she became an instant hero."

"This Madame Moustache was pretty unique," said Prez, reading from his phone. "She might have been the best blackjack dealer in the Old West. Wow! Later, she ended up in Deadwood, and she became friends with Calamity Jane."

"Do you think Grant Marsh ever met Madame Moustache?" Kevin asked.

"It wasn't a very big town," said Kari. "I'll bet anyone who went to Ft. Benton probably knew who Madame Moustache was."

"Okay," said Chad. "What about the two *Mandans*?"

Jack said, "One Mandan refers to the keelboat *Mandan* that's been along the riverfront in Ft. Benton since 1965. It was actually built for a 1952 movie called *The Big Sky*. I've got a photo right here."

Jack showed everyone a photo.

"I remember we studied keelboats when we studied the Lewis and Clark Expedition," said Mike.

THE KEELBOAT *MANDAN* IN THE MOVIE, *THE BIG SKY*; *OVERHOLSER HISTORICAL RESEARCH CENTER, FORT BENTON, MT*

"Yeah," said Katrice. "Remember, to go upstream they had to tow them or use poles. It must have been really tough work."

"What about the second Mandan?" asked Mayor Kern.

"This is interesting," said Doc, looking at some information on her phone. "The second *Mandan* refers to the Mandan snagboat. It was the last steamboat to go up the Missouri River to Ft. Benton, and that happened on June 20, 1921, about five years after Captain Marsh died. The *Mandan* was also the last steamboat Grant Marsh ever rode on in Ft. Benton—and that was on July 15, 1908—but he took the train to Ft. Benton that time. It was pretty cool, because Captain Marsh got a chance to meet with many of his steamboat friends, and they did a lot of talking about the good old days."

THE STEAMBOAT *MANDAN* ON ITS LAST TRIP TO FT. BENTON;
OVERHOLSER HISTORICAL RESEARCH CENTER, FORT BENTON, MT

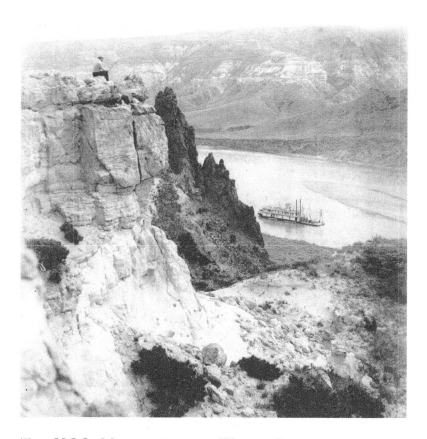

THE U.S.S. MANDAN IN THE WHITE CLIFFS AREA OF THE
MISSOURI BREAKS NATIONAL MONUMENT; *OVERHOLSER
HISTORICAL RESEARCH CENTER, FORT BENTON, MT*

CAPTAIN MARSH ON BOARD THE *MANDAN* ON HIS LAST TRIP TO
FT. BENTON; *OVERHOLSER HISTORICAL RESEARCH CENTER, FORT
BENTON, MT*

"When was the last trip Captain Marsh actually made to Ft. Benton on a steamboat as the pilot and captain?" asked Joletta.

"Egore? Do you know?" Kari asked.

"That would be 1879 on the *F.Y. Batchelor*," Egore replied. "There were 100 Army recruits on board, and they were starting a new fort near Ft. Benton called Ft. Assiniboine."

THE *F.Y. BATCHELOR* ON ITS WAY TO FT. BENTON; *OVERHOLSER HISTORICAL RESEARCH CENTER, FORT BENTON, MT*

Chapter 25

What About Memphis?

They were on the way to Ft. Benton on the *Exercise*.

"I miss Jack Lambert already," said KT.

"Me too," said Kevin.

Prez said, "He had a big linebacker camp for kids he couldn't miss, but he said he'd meet up with us later."

"I sure hope so," said Jessie.

"Hey!" said Mike. "It's too bad, but I get the feeling that whoever's responsible for this history mystery is going to skip Memphis. That kinda makes sense because Grant Marsh lived there for more than 20 years after he left Yankton, but it's not even mentioned much in his biography."

"Did anything really exciting happen while he lived there?" asked Nick.

"At least one thing," said Mike. "He actually lost a steamboat and nearly got killed. It's quite a story."

"Tell us," said Chad.

"Okay. It was the morning of September 17, 1894, and Captain Marsh was on the *Little Eagle, Number Two*, and they were working in the St. Louis area. At the time, they were pushing an empty barge on the river south of St. Louis. At about 11:00 a.m., Captain Marsh glanced to the starboard, which is to the right, and he noticed a very ominous-looking cloud rapidly forming, and the air was absolutely still."

"Tornado!" Kari exclaimed.

"That's right. They called it a cyclone back then. Captain Marsh knew what it was right away. He immediately shouted to his engineer, Charlie DeWitt, through the speaking tube. **'It's a cyclone! Let's try to land as quickly as we can!'**"

"They didn't make it, did they?" Doc guessed.

"No, they didn't have time! In less than 30 seconds, the tornado hit. It caused the steamboat to sway big-time. Captain Marsh shouted into the tube to Charlie Dewitt again, and ordered all hands to run up front and then get on the barge they were pushing before the steamboat was lost. The men did, and it was lucky for them. After that, the *Little Eagle* leaned over so far that the boilers broke off and fell into the river and exploded, shattering the forward hull and deck and tearing the cables that held the barge to the steamer loose."

"Where was Captain Marsh?" asked Nick.

"The captain was still in the pilot house, and he was now cut off from the barge, and his only hope was to get to the rear of the steamboat and try to figure out a way to safety. He was lucky he hadn't been hurt or killed during the explosions with all the flying debris and stuff, but fortunately the strong winds had blown that away from him.

"He climbed through the pilot house window and, as the boat continued to sway, he scrambled upward toward the highest point on the steamboat until, in a moment, the hull was on edge, with the captain clinging to the upturned side. That's when something really amazing happened."

"What?" Jessie was anxious to know.

"There was a big splash as the Little Eagle turned upside down—like a turtle! And somehow, Captain Marsh was able to hold on, and then walk out on the flat bottom of the boat, unharmed, his feet still dry."

"No way!" said Chad.

"That's superhero stuff!" Prez exclaimed.

Mike finished the story, "The barge with the crew on board drifted downstream, and it eventually ended up on the bank of the river, everyone okay. Captain Marsh went for a ride until the overturned boat got stuck on something, and a towboat that was nearby rescued him. ... And after that, Captain Marsh used to joke that that was the only time in steamboating history that someone walked from the pilot house to the bottom of a boat without getting his feet wet."

Chapter 26

The Luella

Prez said, "Look, I've been reading about Grant Marsh's first trip to Ft. Benton, and it has all the qualities of a great story."

"Are there any pretty girls in the story with moustaches?" asked Chad, chuckling.

"There's at least one very pretty girl in the story—but I don't think she has a mustache."

"Is there a *really* bad guy in the story that you love to hate?" Doc inquired.

"Yes. Definitely."

"Buried treasure?" asked Mike.

"Treasure, yes. Buried—maybe not."

"I hope the story has a happy ending," said KT.

"It does."

"Any hunting and fishing?" Kevin asked.

"I know there was some hunting, but I'm sure they did some fishing in the story, too."

"Lots of animals?" asked Nick.

"Many animals, some pretty gross animals," Prez answered with a grimace.

"Flying sharks?" asked Jessie, giggling.

"No flying sharks," Prez answered, making a funny face at Jessie. "Now, are you ready to hear the story?"

"Yes!"

"Okay. This story involves Grant Marsh's first trip ever when he was in charge of a steamboat—both as the captain and the pilot. It takes place in the spring and summer of 1866 on the steamboat *Luella*. It's a pretty long story, so get plenty of popcorn and your favorite beverage before I begin."

They all got popcorn and beverages and returned.

"Okay, we're ready," said Kari.

"All right. Grant Marsh was living in St. Louis at the time. Keep in mind, gold had been discovered in Montana, and lots of people were getting rich quickly. Many people wanted to go there to try their luck at finding some gold, and steamboats were the best way to get there. Ft. Benton was the gateway to the gold mines, so the steamboat business was booming that spring and summer.

"But many of the Sioux Indians were not so thrilled about thousands of white men invading their lands, so there was lots of conflict there. Forts were being built along the way to protect the miners. The steamboats were supplying those forts—another reason why the steamboat business was booming."

"How many forts were there?" asked Nick.

"Let's start at the southern part of where South Dakota is now, which was Ft. Randall. From there to Ft. Benton, which is about 1,300 miles, there were eight forts on the Missouri River. There was Fort Thompson, Fort Sully, Fort Rice, Fort Stevenson, Fort Berthold, Fort Buford, Fort Hawley, and Camp Cooke."

"The *Luella* was attacked by Indians, wasn't it?" asked Nick.

"Let's not jump that far ahead. The *Luella* leaves St. Louis on April 18. It has lots of passengers and over 100 tons of freight on board. It gets as far as Ft. Randall where it hears about Indian attacks between there and Ft. Benton. Thank goodness, the pilot house of the *Luella* was reinforced by iron, so no bullets could get to Grant Marsh and the other pilot on board. But the threat of attack caused lots of fear, and one of the important men on board named Mellon, who was the clerk of the steamboat, got really scared. He got so scared that he actually had to leave the ship near the Milk River in Montana because he was almost having a nervous breakdown. He got on another steamboat and headed back to St. Louis.

"There was something pretty cool about that steamboat Mellon got on. It was the *Rubicon*, and at the time, the *Rubicon* was being run by Captain Horace Bixby—the man who just happened to be one of the greatest steamboat captains *ever* on the *Mississippi* River. He was the one who had taught Mark Twain how to be a great steamboat pilot."

"Too cool," said KT.

"When Mellon was getting on the *Rubicon*, Horace Bixby mentioned to Captain Marsh that someone had called *him* the *Grant Marsh of the lower Mississippi River*. Captain Bixby considered that to be a big compliment because he knew how great a pilot Captain Marsh was. Bixby really didn't like piloting steamboats on the Missouri River. He described it as nothing but a rainwater creek, and he said anyone who can run a steamboat in that river for 20 years, like Grant Marsh did, deserves to be called the *King of Pilots*."

"King of Pilots!" Nick exclaimed. "That would be a good title for a book about Grant Marsh!"

"It would," said Prez. "Now, the *Luella* gets to Wagon Wheel Bluffs, where Bismarck would eventually be built, and everything past that on the Missouri River was new to Captain Marsh. It took all of his skill and luck, but the *Luella* made it to Ft. Benton without any major problems. That was on June 17 or 60 days after they'd left St. Louis."

THE *LUELLA* IN FT. BENTON; *OVERHOLSER HISTORICAL RESEARCH CENTER, FORT BENTON, MT*

"Wow! Two months on the steamboat," said Kevin.

"That's right. And what Grant Marsh saw that first time he was in Ft. Benton was pretty amazing. Imagine a bunch of rough-looking cabins along the river, with lots of rough-looking people coming and going to and from the gold mines and other places. Almost all of the people had some gold in their possession. There were about 500 residents of Ft. Benton who ran the businesses in town."

"I'll bet there was a saloon or two," said Chad.

"Definitely," said Prez.

Chad said, "There also must have been lots of gunfights and crime and stuff, with all that alcohol and gold in town."

"No—and that was one of the things Captain Marsh noticed," said Prez. "Apparently a few years before this, a group of people who were tired of all the lawlessness and crime formed a committee called the Vigilance Committee that dealt with crime problems in a very secretive, very strict way. Once the people in town knew about this, there wasn't much crime taking place. Grant Marsh even told about a deckhand from the *Luella* who'd stolen some medicine when the steamboat was being unloaded—because it contained alcohol. When someone from the Vigilance Committee learned about it, the guy was taken away and given a secret trial one night, then he was whipped severely. After that, Captain Marsh said there were virtually no more crimes on board the *Luella*."

"Pretty harsh stuff," said Chad.

"Undoubtedly," said Prez. "While in Ft. Benton, Captain Marsh and the *Luella* were hired to do a couple of shorter trips—one to Ft. Union, the great fur trading post which was being abandoned at that time. Captain Marsh was hired to bring the goods that were still left at Ft. Union to Ft. Benton. On the second trip, the *Luella* went to a place called Pables Rapids, 70 miles downriver from Ft. Benton, where another steamboat, the *Marion*, got stuck on a sandbar and was a lost cause. Captain Marsh and the crew of the *Luella* rescued the passengers. Marsh bought the machinery, too, and sold it in Ft. Benton when they got back. After that, Captain Marsh had a chance to go on a hunting trip in the Highwood

Mountains nearby with some of the crew and passengers before they started their trip back to St. Louis."

"Did they get anything hunting?" asked Chad.

"Yes, but I couldn't find a lot of specifics," Prez answered. "Grant Marsh said they spent a whole week in an area with lots of game that had probably never been hunted. He said they had a delightful time, and when they got back to Ft. Benton, they were ready for the long trip back … and that's where things got even *more* interesting."

"We still haven't met the pretty girl," said Egore.

"Or the gross animals," added Doc.

"Before you get to that, anyone need a refill on their beverage or some more popcorn?" asked KT.

"I'll help you, KT," said Doc.

"Me, too," said Chad.

When everyone was back in the Steelers Lounge, Prez continued. "The trip back was more action-filled than the trip up the river. … Get this! The *Luella* was loaded with 230 miners and their gold for the trip back—maybe 60 to 80 million dollars' worth of gold in today's money—about three or four million dollars' worth back then. They even had some of the gold packed in metal safes placed in empty wooden kegs that were strapped to the sides of the boat so if the boat got into trouble, the safes would float to the surface. The 230 miners on board were well-armed, too. They were determined to get their gold safely to wherever they were going."

"Pretty amazing," said Mike.

"That's for sure," said Prez. "When the *Luella* left Ft. Benton on September 2, it was the last boat out of Ft. Benton that summer, and it had the most valuable cargo *ever* on the Missouri River. And things went smoothly for the first 347 miles of their journey until they got to the Milk River. Then something pretty strange happened."

"A gang of beautiful girls robbed the steamboat and stole all the gold?" Chad guessed.

"Not quite *that* strange," said Prez. "The *Luella* got stuck on a sandbar, and as the crew was working to get it off, the passengers were watching, standing on the side of the boat. There was one passenger named McClellan who was wearing a leather belt with a lot of his gold dust stored in a concealed area inside the belt, making it really heavy."

"He fell off the boat, didn't he?" KT guessed.

"He did. He fell off the boat into shallow water, but the current was really swift. With all that extra weight of the gold dust in his belt and everything, he just sank, and before anyone could save him, he drowned. They never found him either."

"Yikes!"

"So sad."

"And a few days later, they got to the mouth of the Yellowstone River where they encountered a company of soldiers who were trying to build a new fort named Ft. Buford, near where Ft. Union had been. This was turning out to be a pretty tough task for them. With just a few axes and lots of hard work, they had to try to build a fort using adobe and the cottonwood trees nearby. Much of the time, they were being harassed and attacked by Lakota Sioux Indians. It was a pretty tough life, so you can imagine Grant Marsh's surprise when the *Luella* approached this crummy little fort. You'll never guess who rode down on a horse to greet them?"

"The beautiful girl?" Nick guessed.

Prez laughed. "Finally, you guessed something right. It *was* a beautiful lady. It was the wife of the Captain Rankin, the commander of the post. I'm not sure what her name was, but Captain Marsh described her as a beautiful, young Cuban lady."

"Call her *Samara* instead of Mrs. Rankin," KT suggested.

"Okay. Believe it or not, Samara had come along with her husband to help establish this new fort, despite all the danger and extremely dangerous living conditions. Here she was, out in the middle of nowhere, living through the same hardships as her husband and the other men there.

"Samara had a nice visit with Captain Marsh and some of the others on board the *Luella*—then another exciting and scary thing happened. When Samara was riding her horse back to the small fort from the steamboat, a group of Sioux Indians quickly tried to surround her on their horses. Thankfully, Samara was able to outrun them until her husband and a bunch of the soldiers rushed out from the camp to save her."

"I hope Samara had a long and wonderful life," said KT.

"Well, I can tell you this much. Captain Marsh mentioned that the Captain Rankin and Samara became really good friends, and he stopped there at Ft. Buford anytime he went that way on the river."

Doc said, "It must have been quite a life living in a fort like that, out in the middle of nowhere."

"Really challenging," said Prez. "Words like dangerous, boring, filthy, and extreme were used to describe the conditions inside those early forts. Ft. Buford was very small at first, too, so it was crowded. Imagine spending months in close quarters in the middle of nowhere in forts with no windows, dirt floors, mud roofs, lots of cracks between the cottonwood logs, bed bugs, insects, fleas, mosquitos—and maybe the worst thing of all—*rats*! Thousands and thousands of rats that ate a good share of the food they had stored."

"Are those the gross animals you were referring to?" asked Egore.

"Yes. The rats were unbelievable! At Ft. Rice, for example, the commanding officer reported that the rats ate about 1,000 pounds of their food every day."

"Yikes!" said Nick. "Those are some ravenous rats! Could we please move on down the river now—away from the rats."

Everyone laughed.

"Okay, I will," said Prez, chuckling. "After Ft. Buford, they got stuck on a sandbar near the White Earth River, just 11 miles downriver, and this is where things got a little tricky. You see, they were stuck on a sandbar in a part of the river that had a high bluff on one side, and Sioux Indians appeared soon and started firing at them. That made it difficult to work at getting the boat off the sandbar, so Captain Marsh ordered the passengers to fire at the Indians so the crew could work while the Indians were pinned down. It worked. And they got the steamboat off the sandbar.

"For the next several days, things went pretty smoothly, then something happened. On board the *Luella* was a guy named Gilmore, a boastful bully who got into a quarrel during supper one night. Captain

Marsh realized what was going on, scolded Gilmore, and then threatened to put him on shore and leave him if he didn't shape up.

"Gilmore shaped up for a while because he knew he would certainly be killed by the Sioux Indians if he was left out there by himself. But inside, he just got angrier and angrier. Eventually, he exploded, and he started to tell people he was going to kill Captain Marsh the first chance he got.

"One of the passengers named Paine, who knew Gilmore's intentions, told the captain about this. Grant Marsh wasn't worried. He never thought Gilmore would actually do anything. But Paine gave Captain Marsh his pistol, just in case.

"In a few days, the *Luella* was out of the worst Sioux Indian territory below Ft. Randall and several passengers, including Gilmore, were on shore doing a broad jump contest in the sand. Captain Marsh was out with the crew looking for wood, and he came across this group.

"Gilmore grabbed a revolver from one his friends and said something like, 'Just watch me make that dog of a captain jump!'

"By this time, Captain Marsh had had enough. He told Gilmore he'd heard enough, and it was time to settle things for good. Then he challenged Gilmore to a pistol duel. When Gilmore suddenly backed down, Captain Marsh slapped him in the face and called him a coward. Captain Marsh probably would have killed Gilmore after that, but Paine held him back, saying, 'Don't kill him! He's a coward!'"

"Did they ever fight again after that?" asked Chad.

"No. Grant Marsh actually tried to settle things

with Gilmore. When they got to Sioux City, he offered to buy Gilmore a drink, but Gilmore refused. … The rest of the trip went smoothly and they got into St. Louis on October 5. Grant Marsh made 24,000 dollars on that trip."

Chapter 27

Ft. Benton History Walk

Everyone except Egore was sleeping when they landed in Great Falls, Montana, a little before 4:00 a.m. that morning. Egore woke everyone up so they could get ready to board the *Flying Teddy* before they flew to Ft. Benton.

As they flew the remaining 40 miles to Ft. Benton on the *Flying Teddy*, Prez said, "I like the mayor's idea of us getting there really early so we can walk with him along the old steamboat levee before things start to get crazy in town."

Chad asked, "Is the mayor going to be there when we land?"

"Yes."

"When is sunrise in Montana this time of the year anyway?" asked Jessie, yawning.

"About 5:40," said Egore. "Remember, we're in the Mountain Time Zone now."

"Look at that long line of cars down there—as far as the eyes can see," said Nick. "All those lights make it look like some sort of giant light snake on the prairie."

"I'd rather you not mention snakes," said KT cringing. "I hate snakes!"

"Sorry," said Nick. "So do I."

When they got close to the town, they couldn't help but notice how beautiful Ft. Benton looked from the air, with the all the lights coming from the town, the location right next to the river, and the beautiful hills nearby.

"I can already see why Ft. Benton has been picked as one of the prettiest towns in America," said Kari.

"It's spectacular!" said Jessie.

PHOTO COURTESY OF BURNT IMAGE PHOTOGRAPHY, FT. BENTON, MT

FT. BENTON, 1912; *PHOTOGRAPH BY EVELYN J. CAMERON IN THE BOOK "FORT BENTON" BY KEN ROBISON*

THE STEAMBOAT *BENTON* DOCKED UPRIVER IN FT. BENTON, 1878; *OVERHOLSER HISTORICAL RESEARCH CENTER, FORT BENTON, MT*

A lithograph from a sketch by Gustav Sohon of Ft. Benton, 1860; *Overholser Historical Research Center, Fort Benton, MT*

With just a hint of twilight, they landed in the park by the river, near a reconstruction of the actual fort named Fort Benton. The fort had been founded in 1846, before the steamboats came to the area, and it was once an important fur and buffalo robe trading post.

As they were landing, KT said, "Look at all the campers and tents! I'm glad we came early."

"This is going to be a crazy fun day!" added Kevin.

When they got off the *Flying Teddy,* the mayor of Ft. Benton, Rhett Knox, was there to greet them.

"Welcome to Ft. Benton, birthplace of Montana!" said Mayor Knox.

Kari was first to greet the mayor. "Thanks so much, Mayor," she said, as she shook his hand and then introduced everyone.

Mayor Knox said, "Sarabiskota, we're so happy to have you here in Ft. Benton. This day promises to be one of the most exciting in Ft. Benton history, and I'm so happy you will be part of it. I thought we would start the morning off right by taking a walk along the old steamboat levee where Grant Marsh once parked his steamboats. There are a bunch of historic landmarks, statues, and monuments along the way that I'll be able to tell you about, and hopefully, answer most of your questions. It's about one mile to the Grand Union Hotel, where you'll be staying tonight. We can stop there for breakfast when we're done, and I've made sure you can also check in early if you'd like. After that, we can explore Main Street and the rest of the town if you want to."

"Perfect!"

"Thanks."

Many other early risers followed them as they slowly walked the trail along the river. The sun rose on a perfectly clear morning soon after they started, adding to the beauty of their walk.

They saw so many interesting things along the way. Early in their walk, they stopped at the keelboat *Mandan* and took a group photo. Many people wanted to have photos taken with Sarabiskota, so they were there for quite a while.

Not too far from the *Mandan*, they came across a memorial to a former governor of Montana, and that got their attention right away. The inscription on the memorial said the governor had drowned near there under mysterious circumstances in 1867. His name was General Thomas Francis Meagher.

"What was this all about?" asked Kevin.

"It's one of my favorite mysteries," replied Mayor Knox. "Meagher was quite a character. He was Irish and he has been described as being truculent, verbose, belligerent, and brash. He was definitely a guy that could stir up trouble and could make enemies, but he was also a real leader. He lived a pretty incredible life that included things like being banished to the island of Tasmania for treason, escaping there and coming to New York, eventually becoming a Civil War hero, then coming here to Montana when he was appointed by President Andrew Johnson as the secretary of the new Montana Territory. Not long after that, he became acting governor while the real governor went to Washington, D.C., on business for the new territory. But something bizarre happened right here in 1867 that's a big mystery.

GOVERNOR THOMAS FRANCIS MEAGHER; *OVERHOLSER HISTORICAL RESEARCH CENTER, FORT BENTON, MT*

"On June 30, 1867, the steamboat *G.A. Thomson* came to town, and Governor Meagher came the next day to pick up some rifles from the boat. At the time, he was not only the acting governor, but he was leader of a militia that was protecting a trail nearby from Sioux Indian attack. That night, Meagher apparently had a good time having dinner with friends in town, and he drank quite a bit, as he often did. Afterward, he returned to the *G.A. Thomson* to get some sleep—and that's where something happened—but no one knows exactly what that was. A watchman on the steamboat saw someone fall from the upper deck of the steamboat, then there was a thorough search up and down the river, but it never turned up anything. They never found Governor Meagher or any sign of him—*ever*."

"What do you think happened to him?" asked Egore.

"I don't know what to think," said Mayor Knox. "Some people think he was drunk and lost his balance, and he fell into the river and drowned. Some think he was killed and thrown overboard. ... He definitely had lots of enemies."

"Was Captain Grant Marsh near Ft. Benton when this happened?" asked Kari.

"I don't know," the mayor replied.

Everyone looked at Egore.

Egore said, "Grant Marsh was definitely in the area. He was in Ft. Benton with the *Ida Stockdale* on June 29, 1867, but I'm not sure if he was still in town when this happened on July 1. Remember, the *Ida Stockdale* was the boat Captain Marsh was on that summer when they came across that huge herd of buffalo."

Prez had a determined, inquisitive look in his eyes. Kari winced. "Don't try to solve this while we're in town," she said. "We're here for other reasons."

"Oh, I won't," Prez answered. "I just think it's a great mystery."

As they walked farther, they got to the Ft. Benton Bridge, now a walking bridge.

"This reminds me of the Meridian Bridge in Yankton," said Kevin. "Do we have time to walk on it right now?"

"Sure," answered the mayor. "We've got plenty of time. I'm sure it's going to be really crowded later, so this is probably the best time possible. This bridge was built in 1888, about nine years after Grant Marsh's last trip here on steamboat. It was the first bridge to span the Missouri River in Montana. It actually once had a span that swung open to let steamboats pass. A flood in 1908 collapsed the swing span, and it was replaced in 1921. Now, of course, it's a walking bridge, and I love walking across it almost every morning."

FT. BENTON BRIDGE, *AUTHOR'S PHOTO*

FT. BENTON BRIDGE, *AUTHOR'S PHOTO*

The steamer O. K. coming through the "draw" bridge at Fort Benton, Mont.

THE STEAMBOAT O.K. AT THE FT. BENTON BRIDGE WITH THE SWING SPAN OPEN IN 1907; *FROM THE BOOK "FORT BENTON" BY KEN ROBISON*

After they got off the bridge, they came to a beautiful statue of a dog named Shep.

"What's the deal with Shep?" asked Mike.

"I love his story," said the mayor. "The story begins in August of 1936, so it's about 20 years after Grant Marsh died. A sheepherder got sick while he was tending his flock, and he was taken to the hospital in Ft. Benton. An old sheep dog named Shep had followed the sheepherder into town, and soon he camped out by the hospital door. A kind nun fed him the next few days, and the man, sadly, died.

"The man's body was then put on an east-bound train by an undertaker, as the big shepherd dog watched. The dog whined as the train pulled away from the station. From that day on, for the next five-and-a-half years, Shep met four trains a day, took a good look at each passenger, then many times he was chased off. Shep did this every day, and eventually his fame spread. The railroad employees liked him a lot and fed him. The passengers loved him too. Eventually, one cold winter, after Shep had lost much of his hearing, he died. On the fiftieth anniversary of his death, a sculptor was hired to make this memorial to Shep."

"That's a wonderful story!" said Doc, with tears in her eyes.

"I love that story," said Mike.

"Me, too," said Mayor Knox. "Now, let's head over here to the Grand Union Hotel for some breakfast."

SHEP MEETING A TRAIN; *FROM THE BOOK "FORT BENTON" BY KEN ROBISON*

THE BRONZE STATUE OF SHEP IN FT. BENTON; *FROM THE BOOK "FORT BENTON" BY KEN ROBISON*

THE GRAND UNION HOTEL, *AUTHOR'S PHOTOS*

Chapter 28

Grand Union Breakfast

When they walked into the Grand Union Hotel, it was like going back in time to the 1880s.

THE GRAND UNION HOTEL, *AUTHOR'S PHOTOS*

THE GRAND UNION HOTEL, *AUTHOR'S PHOTOS*

"This is incredible!" said KT.

"I feel like we could be meeting Grant Marsh for breakfast," said Jessie.

"Wouldn't that be awesome," said Nick. "But I want Madame Moustache to be there, too."

"I'll bet the two of them could tell us some good stories," said Doc.

They walked into the dining room, and they were greeted by a friendly, middle-aged man named Duane Roth.

"Welcome Mayor Knox and Sarabiskota! We're all so honored to have you here this morning. I'm Duane Roth, and I'll be your head waiter this morning. We have our largest table reserved for you. You're going to enjoy our best view of the Missouri River."

Duane showed them over to their table. After they were seated, he said, "I'm a bit of a history buff and I've really enjoyed keeping up with all of your Grant Marsh information on Spacebook."

"Thanks," said Kari. "Would you please tell us a little about the history of this wonderful hotel?"

"Sure," said Duane, "the Grand Union is the oldest operating hotel in Montana. The hotel first opened in November of 1882, which was actually seven years before Montana became a state. At the time, it was considered the best hotel between Chicago and Seattle. It cost $50,000 to build, and it ran for more than 100 years after it first opened. However, it went through some tough times, and it had to close in the mid-1980s. It was empty and getting in pretty rough shape until the Gagnons, Jim and Cheryl, began to restore it in 1997. Then it reopened on November 2, 1999, which was the 117th anniversary of its first opening."

"Do you know how long it took to build?" asked Nick.

"Yes. One year, three months, and 18 days. When it opened in 1882, they had a huge party to celebrate, where over 300 attended. From everything I've been reading about Captain Marsh, he was not there for the opening, but we know he stayed here when he came back in July of 1908 by train to meet the snagboat *Mandan* and see many of his old steamboat friends."

As soon as they opened their menus, they got a big surprise.

"There's a special Captain Marsh breakfast!"

"There's a Madame Moustache breakfast!"

"A Sarabiskota breakfast, too!"

"This is so cool!"

Duane explained, "When we found out what was going to happen here in Ft. Benton today, and that you were staying here at our hotel, we knew this was going to be a very special day, so we designed and printed these up late last night. Kinley Small, the graphic artist who did most of the work, actually works here in the hotel."

"Please thank her for us," said Prez.

"You might be able to do that in person," said Duane. "She will be working at the front desk later today."

While they were eating, Kari said, "Mayor Knox, we've read where Grant Marsh is often referred to as the Steamboat King of Montana Rivers because of all the things he accomplished on the rivers of Montana without ever losing a steamboat. But, with all the monuments and statues and memorials along our walk this morning, I don't think I saw anything honoring Captain Marsh."

"You're right," said Mayor Knox. "There should be something along there to honor him. I've got a strong feeling that the people responsible for all this excitement we've had the past several days just might correct that situation today."

"I think you're right," said Prez. "I can't wait to see what's in store for Ft. Benton today."

"It's going to be fun," said Egore.

Mayor Knox looked across the table at Mike. "Speaking of fun, my wife and kids and I can't wait to hear you sing at the park later today."

"Thank you so much," said Mike. "I'm really looking forward to it. For the first time, I'm going to try to sing the entire song I've written about this Grant Marsh adventure."

Chapter 29

Something's Fishy in Ft. Benton

What an amazing day it was in Ft. Benton! Sarabiskota had a great time exploring the town, meeting people from all over the world—many of them wearing fake moustaches. Others tried to dress up to look like Grant Marsh, "X" Beidler, Mark Twain, Sitting Bull, Fast Walker, or Egore.

Doc giggled. "I can only imagine what Halloween is going to be like this year."

As the day went on, Sarabiskota joined the thousands of people gathered in Old Fort Park. They all had a great time listening to some excellent entertainment and meeting people from all over the world.

Right before sunset, Mike was introduced, followed by a huge round of applause and plenty of screaming. Mike spoke in his perfect Elvis voice, "Thank you. Thank you very much. I can't imagine having more fun than we've had the last several days—and today has been just GREAT!"

The people cheered and cheered.

"Special thanks to all the friendly people here in Ft. Benton for being such great hosts and for making this all possible. How many of you have had as much fun today as I have?"

There was more enthusiastic cheering.

"I wrote a little song that might help remind us of this incredible journey we've been on the past few days. I hope you like it. ... I have a strong feeling that whoever is responsible for this whole Grant Marsh adventure is probably listening to us right now—you're probably even in this audience." Mike giggled. "They might be standing right next to you at this very moment."

Everyone in the audience looked around at the people around them, just wondering. JB and Madison were standing near the stage. They did the same thing, acting like innocent bystanders.

Mike continued, "Anyway, thanks to whoever you are for this fun adventure we've been on. I'd like to dedicate this song to you. If you'd like to, it would be perfect timing if you presented your next big surprise when I'm finished with this song."

JB and Madison looked at each other and smiled. Mike began singing a beautiful song in his amazing Elvis voice:

Now we know there is no mys-tery,
Grant Marsh is the greatest steamboatman in his-tory!
But we still got a mighty big mys-tery.
Who's got us learning all this Grant Marsh his-tory?
And I'd really really like to know for sure,
Where are we headed next on this history tour?

This all started in Mandan and Bismarck,
The *Far West* suddenly appeared on the river,
Then it took off into the air at Ft. Abraham Lincoln,
A huge surprise it sure did deliver.

The Pittsburgh area was our next destination.
Grant Marsh threw rocks at steamboats as a kid.
He always dreamed of working on a steamboat,
And at 12 years of age—that's exactly what he did!

Then we were off to St. Louis,
Where young Grant Marsh was saved by Mark Twain,
And he got married to Katy,
An apple-butter stirring, partially to blame.

Then we headed to Yankton,
Where we got a huge surprise,
Captain Marsh and the *Far West* flew up on the bridge,
Right before our very eyes!

Now we're in Ft. Benton,
Historic and beautiful—this town's number one!
Don't you wish Grant Marsh and Madame Moustache
could be here right now,
To join in all the fun!?

Now we know there is no mystery,
Grant Marsh is the greatest steamboatman in his-tory!
But we still got a mighty big mys-tery.
Who's got us learning all this Grant Marsh his-tory?
And I'd really like to know for sure,
Where are we headed next on this Captain Marsh
history tour?

When Mike was finished singing his song, there was tremendous applause. While this was going on, people started to notice some commotion downriver.

"Look!"

"Two steamboats are approaching, side by side!"

"There are two steamboats coming up the river!"

Yes, there *were* two beautiful steamboats, all lit up beautifully in multicolored lights, approaching them from downriver.

Suddenly a voice that sounded a lot like the famous announcer Will Volk came over the large speakers in the park. "Maybe they weren't nearly as fast as NASCAR races, but there were steamboat races up and down the river in Ft. Benton's heyday, and Captain Grant Marsh took part in several of them. People along the riverbanks used to bet on them. They'd even try to bribe the crews and captains on the steamboats to break records. Steamboat racing probably wasn't very safe, especially when the rivers were low, but they did it anyway. When steamboats set speed records, they didn't win a ton of money. Instead, they got a set of elk antlers which they hung them in the front of the pilot house.

"Right now you're watching replicas of the *Nellie Peck* and the *Far West* approach us, and these two boats were involved in one of the greatest steamboat races of all-time, way back in 1872. The Coulson Company had built two new boats especially for the upper Missouri River. They quickly proved to be the fastest boats on the Missouri. The *Far West* had Captain Coulson and pilots named Comfort and Sims. The *Nellie Peck* had Captain Grant Marsh on board along with another pilot named John LaBarge.

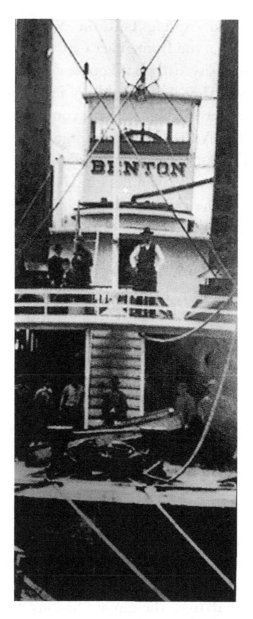

THE STEAMER *BENTON* WITH THE HORNS BETWEEN HER STACKS IN FRONT OF THE PILOT HOUSE; *OVERHOLSER HISTORICAL RESEARCH CENTER, FORT BENTON, MT*

"In the early spring, both the *Nellie Peck* and *Far West* had made a run from Sioux City to Ft. Benton and back to Sioux City. They both got back to Sioux City at about the same time in the middle of June—and the race was on! The river was high, and the conditions were great for speed. The *Nellie Peck* had a larger cargo and more stops, but Captain Marsh's boat kept a lead for the first 1,370 miles. But just 103 miles from here, the *Nellie Peck* was passed by the *Far West*. It got to Ft. Benton several hours ahead of the *Nellie Peck* and unloaded its cargo. The *Far West* set a new record of 17 days, 20 hours.

"Captain Marsh didn't let that bother him. When they got here to Ft. Benton, they unloaded the *Nellie Peck* as fast as they could, determined to beat the *Far West* back to Sioux City. The *Far West* got an early lead, because it was first to unload its cargo in Ft. Benton. There was no stopping for both boats, except for wood, and they traveled day and night. Near Ft. Berthold, the people on board the *Nellie Peck* spotted smoke from the *Far West*. The soldiers at the fort cheered, and the American Indians at the fort looked on with wonder.

"Once the *Nellie Peck* passed the *Far West*, Captain Marsh was determined to keep the lead, so he stayed on the wheel as long as possible. They got all the way to South Dakota to an easy stretch of the river, and Captain Marsh needed some rest, so he turned the wheel over to his partner, LaBarge. The captain had just barely gotten to sleep when the watchman ran to his cabin and gave him some startling news—the steamboat had gone aground.

"Captain Marsh couldn't believe it! The steamboat was actually off course. The cub pilot was so mad at

LaBarge, he pulled out his pistol and was ready to shoot him. But Captain Marsh took the revolver and threw it in the river.

"They tried to free the *Nellie Peck*, but they were eventually passed. Although the *Nellie Peck* wasn't the first boat back to Sioux City, it actually had a better time—five days and 23 hours.

"Now! Watch where the *Nellie Peck* and the *Far West* are going!"

Suddenly, the two steamboats, with lights flashing, flew into the air and landed next to each other on the middle span of the Ft. Benton Bridge. It was a magnificent sight!

"What's that?!" someone screamed, pointing into the air about 200 yards east of the bridge.

It was unbelievable! A large, beautifully lit statue of Grant Marsh slowly flew through the air toward the bridge like Superman, and then it landed feetfirst, between the two steamboats on the bridge.

"AHHHHHHHHHHHH!"

The announcer continued, "Where will we be tomorrow to *finish* this wonderful Grant Marsh adventure? Walk over a little closer to the river and you will find out!"

The huge crowd walked closer to the river. The light coming from the three objects on the bridge provided enough light for everyone to walk safely.

When the crowd was in position, things started to happen. The river suddenly lit up with what looked like hundreds of small fish near the surface of the water.

"They're little light fish!" someone called out.

"It's beautiful!" a little girl cried out.

"Look at all the colors!"

"They're forming a picture!"

"It's the Capitol in Bismarck!"

"They're swimming around *again*!"

"They're forming another picture!"

"It's the Mandan Train Depot!"

"They're swimming around *again*!"

"It's the Custer House!"

Nick turned to his friends, "Oh boy! We're going back to where this all started!"

Chapter 30

A Note Under the Door

After all the excitement in the park, Sarabiskota headed back to the Grand Union Hotel. Not long after that, they met in the largest suite in the hotel, where all the girls were staying.

"Let's order a couple of pizzas from room service!" Chad suggested.

"I'm on it," said Kari. "I'll order three large."

"Thanks."

"What a night!" Doc exclaimed.

"Whoever's doing all of this is unbelievable!" said Chad. "Those fish topped it all!"

"Mike, *you* were unbelievable, too!" Jessie added.

All of his Sarabiskota friends clapped enthusiastically.

"Thanks!"

KT sighed. "And now we're headed back to where it all started—Mandan and Bismarck and Ft. Lincoln! I'm really going to hate seeing this all come to an end."

"Do you think we're finally going to find out who's responsible for all of this?" asked Mike.

"If my theory is correct, we will," said Kari, "because I'm more convinced than ever that the people who are doing all this are doing it to get *our* attention."

"If that's true, they sure have succeeded," said Prez.

"Big time!" said Doc.

Nick said, "So, I know Captain Marsh eventually came back to North Dakota and the Bismarck-Mandan area after he lived in Memphis, but I don't know the details."

Everyone looked at Egore.

Egore said, "He had lived in Memphis for over 20 years, but he really missed working on the Upper Missouri River. But there really weren't any opportunities for work on steamboats there until something happened in 1901 when Grant Marsh would have been about 67 years old. That year, a wealthy man named General W.D. Washburn from Minneapolis, a former United States Senator who owned several flour mills, started a huge operation north of Bismarck—and he needed Captain Marsh to help run his steamboats."

"What do you mean—*huge operation?*" asked KT.

"General Washburn bought over 100,000 acres of good farmland along the Missouri River, plus he had a coal mine, plus there was a railroad line through his land that went right down to the Missouri River where the town of Washburn grew up. He also had several boats and barges—including two steamboats—to trade lumber, wheat, and other things up and down the Missouri River. Captain Marsh helped operate the steamboats."

Chad said, "It must have been so cool when Grant Marsh saw how much North Dakota had changed since he left in the early 1880s."

THE *EXPANSION* AND *FRAYNE* AT THE WASHBURN LANDING, 1916;
STATE HISTORICAL SOCIETY OF NORTH DAKOTA

THE *EXPANSION* AND *SCARAB* TIED UP AT DOCK AT WASHBURN
LANDING, ABOUT 1910; *STATE HISTORICAL SOCIETY OF NORTH DAKOTA*

"Undoubtedly," said Egore. "When Grant Marsh got back, he couldn't believe it. When he left in the early 1880s, the whole area was basically wilderness, with an occasional little town and an isolated farmer or two, barely making a living. When he returned more than 20 years later, there were many little towns, with farms all over the place that were growing wheat and other crops. When he'd left, Bismarck wasn't the capital of *anything*, and now it was the capital of the new state of North Dakota. And both Mandan and Bismarck had changed a *bunch*! The beautiful Northern Pacific Railroad Bridge had been built between the two cities, and the railroad was helping the whole area grow. There was even some phone service and electric lights. Bismarck had more than 5,000 people. Mandan was a thriving town, too, but Ft. Abraham Lincoln was abandoned, and anything of any value, like the lumber, had been taken away by the settlers."

THE STEAMBOAT *BISMARCK* AND THE NORTHERN PACIFIC BRIDGE, ABOUT 1905; *STATE HISTORICAL SOCIETY OF NORTH DAKOTA*

The steamboats *Expansion* and *Washburn* at the Bismarck
Landing, with the *Weston* out on the river, about 1906;
State Historical Society of North Dakota

The *Weston* and the *Deapolis* at the Bismarck landing,
about 1908; *State Historical Society of North Dakota*

"And Teddy was President of the United States then, right?" asked Nick.

"That's right. Teddy actually came back to North Dakota about the same time that Grant Marsh came back to North Dakota. He spoke at the Capitol in Bismarck and at the Mandan Train Depot on April 7, 1903."

"I'll bet Grant Marsh showed up to see Teddy if he was anywhere nearby," said Mike.

PRESIDENT THEODORE ROOSEVELT SPEAKING AT THE NORTH DAKOTA CAPITOL ON APRIL 7, 1903; *STATE HISTORICAL SOCIETY OF NORTH DAKOTA*

"I agree," said Egore, "but I haven't been able to find any evidence of that yet. ... Captain Marsh worked for General Washburn until the spring of 1904, then Washburn sold his railroad and two steamboats and barges to the Minneapolis, St. Paul & Sault Ste. Marie Railroad Company. Then the railroad sold the steamboats and barges to a man named Captain Isaac Baker from Bismarck, and Captain Marsh went to work for Baker. Captain Baker and Grant Marsh became good lifetime friends after that. Eventually Baker formed the Benton Packet Company, and it had six steamboats, six barges, and two ferry boats. Grant Marsh operated all of the steamboats at one time or the other."

"Hey!" Kevin said. "Someone just slipped something under the door!"

"Quick!" yelled Kari. "Check the hall!"

Chad and Kevin got to the door in a flash and opened it up. They went out into the hall, but it was empty.

On the way back into the room, Chad picked up a small envelope by the door and handed it to Kari. Kari opened it up and pulled out a note.

"What does it say?" asked Doc anxiously.

Kari said, "It says, *Hope you all are having fun learning about Captain Grant Marsh. We hope to see you all at A&B Pizza in Mandan tomorrow at midnight. We'll buy. We'll answer all your questions then.* It's signed *Friends.*"

"Wow!" said Jessie. "Tomorrow is *really* going to be interesting!"

Chapter 31

On the Way to North Dakota

By 9:00 a.m. the next morning, they were in the Steelers Lounge on board the *Exercise*, flying over the Missouri River just west of Williston, North Dakota. They were following the Missouri River back to the Bismarck-Mandan area.

"I've got a question for all of you," said Kevin. "Knowing all we know now about Captain Marsh ... if you could spend any one day with him, during his entire life, which day would you choose? ... Ladies, you may go first. Let's go right around the room starting with you, Kari."

"This is really tough," said Kari. "The first day that comes to mind—I'd like to be there for the apple-butter stirring ... or maybe the first day he worked on a steamboat. I guess I'll go with the first day of work on a steamboat, when he was only 12, because I'd really like to meet him when he was a boy."

"Good one, Kari," said Kevin. "How about you, Jessie?"

"Umm … okay, I'd like to spend an entire day with Captain Marsh and his family when they were living in Yankton. I'd like to get to know the whole family, and what they did on a typical day when Captain Marsh wasn't working."

"Good one."

"KT?"

"I want to spend the day with him that day the tornado turns the boat over—provided I survive the incident."

Everyone laughed.

"Dangerous choice," said Kevin. "Doc?"

"I would choose one of the days they're coming back to Ft. Abraham Lincoln after the Little Big Horn. I know it would be intense, but I'd like to meet Dr. Porter and Captain Marsh then, and see how they were able to handle such a challenging experience."

"Excellent. Your turn, Mike."

"I'd like to be on the boat with him the first time he traveled past the area on the river that would become Bismarck and Mandan—when they called it Wagon Wheel Bluff or Wagon Wheel Bluffs. I would love to see that."

"Chad?"

"I want to be there when Captain Marsh goes up against Fast Walker. I would like to see how long I could keep up with those guys, and just how fast that Fast Walker was. I think I could beat him."

That remark got lots of laughs.

"I'm betting on Fast Walker by ten miles," said KT.

Everyone laughed.

"Nick, you're next."

"I have to go with the day they saw the zillions of buffalo. That must have been incredible!"

"Egore?"

"I would like to spend any day with Grant Marsh in the pilot house, operating a steamboat on the Missouri River—maybe I'd choose the last day he *ever* commanded a steamboat. Can you even imagine how much fun it would be to talk to him about his life?"

"Great one, Egore," said Kevin. "How about you, Prez?"

"As much as I'd like to be there when Samuel Clemens saved Captain Marsh's life, I'd choose the day Teddy first met Grant Marsh, since we're not sure when that first happened. To meet those two great men that day would be a dream come true for me."

Kari said, "How about you, Kevin?"

"I want to be there one of the days they went hunting that summer they were on the steamboat *Luella*. It's hard to imagine hunting in a place that almost no one had ever seen before."

"That was awesome," said Kari. "Did anyone find anything exciting that happened to Captain Marsh after he left Memphis and came back to North Dakota?"

Prez said, "There's one incident I found that was pretty unbelievable. Captain Marsh had never done anything like it before with a steamboat. I wonder if anyone had *ever* done it with a steamboat. ... You know how sandbars form on the river all the time?"

"Thank goodness," said Nick. "They're so much fun."

"Well," Prez continued, "back in 1905, a sandbar about 200 feet long formed along the bank of the

Missouri River in a really bad place. It totally blocked the intake pipe for the water plant that supplied the water for town of Bismarck and for the Northern Pacific Railroad there."

"Yikes!" said Nick.

"Not good at all," said Prez. "Who do you think they called on to get rid of the sandbar?"

"Grant Marsh, of course," said Chad. "But how can he get rid of a sandbar with a steamboat?"

"That's what he thought, too. It really was an unbelievable effort, and much of Bismarck and Mandan watched it unfold on a Sunday morning, starting at about 11:00. It was a little more complicated than this, but Grant Marsh basically backed the steamboat *Weston* up to the end of the sandbar at its farthest point upriver. Then, using the paddlewheel like a scoop, he dug a channel through the sand so the river could then basically help wash the sandbar away. It definitely wasn't easy for Captain Marsh. At one point, he almost got the *Weston* stuck in the middle of the sandbar, but he was able to work himself free. By the middle of the afternoon that day, the sandbar was half gone. By the next afternoon, it was almost all gone."

"Captain Marsh saves the day!" said Chad.

"That's for sure," said Mike. "It's hard to imagine what they would have done about that sandbar and their water situation if he hadn't been there."

Doc said, "I found some other stuff about Captain Marsh when he lived in Bismarck, and it's a little sad. He had some pretty tough times the last ten years of his life. The first really awful thing happened in 1906. Katy died. The two of them had been together for 46 years."

"That's so sad," said KT.

"A year later," said Doc, "Grant Marsh actually lost his steamboat pilot's license for about a year when something pretty strange happened."

"What!?" Nick exclaimed.

"I'm going to tell Grant Marsh's version of the story, based on what I could find out so far. After all we've learned about Grant Marsh, I think we all know that he had strong character, and he was someone that got along with almost everyone. Well, there was another steamboat pilot named William Massie, who Grant Marsh had known for a long time—they had actually piloted some of the same steamboats, including the *Far West*. For some reason, this Massie guy and Grant Marsh didn't like each other at all, and it led to an incident on board a steamboat on the river in Bismarck. According to Grant Marsh, Massie had been saying some nasty things about him behind his back, things that also offended Grant Marsh's mother. When Captain Marsh heard about this, he boarded the steamboat *Weston* on the Missouri River near Bismarck to confront Massie."

"They ended up fighting, didn't they?" Mike guessed.

"They did. Grant Marsh said Massie started it. Massie claimed Grant Marsh did. Grant Marsh admitted he eventually threw a sugar bowl at Massie—and he also admitted it was a pretty heavy sugar bowl."

"A sugar bowl attack?" Nick said, giggling.

Everyone laughed.

Doc continued. "Whatever actually happened, Massie pressed charges to some pilot licensing board, and they decided in Massie's favor—and Captain Marsh lost his license for about a year."

"Disgusting," said Nick.

"That must have been a very difficult year for Grant Marsh," said KT. "He'd just recently lost his wife, and then he loses his license to work."

"No doubt," said Doc. "But I have to tell you something else about that Massie guy that you're not going to believe."

"He was married to Madame Moustache?" Nick said, giggling.

Everyone laughed. Doc said, "That would be interesting, but Madame Mustache had better taste than that. No, Massie actually had the bullet that killed Wild Bill Hickok in his wrist till the day he died."

"No way!" Mike exclaimed.

"He did," said Doc. "Captain Massie was part of that poker game in Deadwood, South Dakota, in August of 1876 when someone snuck up behind Wild Bill Hickok and shot him in the head. The bullet went right through Wild Bill and lodged in Captain Massie's wrist—where it stayed until he died in 1910. The doctors at the time probably figured it would do more harm than good to take it out."

"That's crazy," said Jessie.

"Did Grant Marsh know Wild Bill Hickok?" asked Kevin.

"Yes, he did," Doc answered. "Captain Marsh considered Wild Bill a friend."

"This just keeps getting more and more interesting," said Jessie.

Prez said, "I've looked at some of the newspaper articles from the last ten years or so of Grant Marsh's life. It appears Captain Marsh just kept working on steamboats. In 1908, he mentioned wanting to retire, possibly to Miles City, Montana. For some reason, though, he didn't have enough money to retire."

WILD BILL HICKOK, *AUTHOR'S COLLECTION*

"I thought he made all that money as a steamboat captain," said Nick.

"He did" said Prez. "Who knows what happened to all of it. All I know, Grant Marsh was still working on steamboats when he was over 80. That's pretty amazing."

"Where did Grant Marsh live in Bismarck?" asked Chad.

After a few seconds, everyone looked at Egore.

"Believe it or not," said Egore, "he lived on a houseboat on the Missouri River in Bismarck, below where the Grant Marsh Bridge is now located, and he ate most of his meals with the men who worked for his good friend Captain Baker. I actually found a photo of a houseboat from that location and time, but I can't be sure it's Grant Marsh's houseboat."

PHOTO OF THE HOUSEBOAT AT THE BISMARCK LANDING FROM ABOUT 1909; *STATE HISTORICAL SOCIETY OF NORTH DAKOTA*

"I'm betting he didn't stay on that houseboat during the coldest winter weather," said Kevin.

Egore said, "I found some newspaper articles about him traveling to St. Louis and other places in the winter. He had plenty of friends in Bismarck if he needed to get out of some really bad winter weather while he was living on the houseboat. ... I found a few other newspaper articles about Captain Marsh that you also might find interesting."

"Please, Egore," said Kari. "Tell us."

"I found a newspaper story from late May in 1907 that tells about Grant Marsh's pleasure yacht *Irene* going into commission in May of 1907—near the Northern Pacific Railroad Bridge. It took people on pleasure trips. The charge was 13 cents an hour. Children under twelve, when accompanied by a parent, were free. ... From the year 1912—he's telephoning the *Bismarck Tribune* on December 3, to tell them the river has frozen over. ... There were a couple of articles from the year before he died. There's one from July of 1915 that has Captain Marsh arriving in Bismarck, and he's in charge of the steamboats *Dakota* and *Montana*, loaded with 20,000 pounds of dynamite and 60,000 pounds of gunpowder, headed for St. Louis."

"Yikes!" Chad exclaimed.

"It even mentions in the article that he probably was going to go as far as Sioux City, but because of his poor health, he wasn't likely to go on to St. Louis. ... There's one from the middle of August in 1915, just about five months before Captain Marsh dies. He's on a short trip up the river on a steamboat named the *Scarab* with his good friend Captain Isaac Baker and a bunch of people, including the governor and a former governor of North Dakota. On that trip, Grant Marsh told stories about his life including the Little Big Horn which had occurred 39 years before this."

Chad spoke more quietly than usual. "So, Grant Marsh was pretty active all the way till the end of his life."

"He sure was," said Mike. "Talk about living life to the fullest."

KT said, "I know we found out a long time ago that

Grant Marsh died on January 2, 1916, but where is he buried?

Prez said, "Remember, Grant Marsh always wanted to be buried on Wagon Wheel Bluff, above the railroad bridge. Well, sadly, that didn't happen. Grant Marsh died and was buried in the St. Mary's Cemetery in Bismarck in a grave with no headstone. He even had some debts that his friend Captain Baker tried to pay off by selling Grant Marsh's houseboat and other possessions. But something really good happened about 42 years after Grant Marsh died. In 1958, a teacher from Bismarck named Pat DeForest brought attention to the fact that Grant Marsh was buried in an unmarked grave, and he suggested a nice marker be placed there. After that, the Captain Grant Marsh Memorial Committee was formed, and they got contributions from pioneer families and friends who were interested in seeing that the captain's grave was marked.

"On Memorial Day in 1960 there was a service to mark the placing of a special headstone over the grave. About 60 people attended the service that day at the St. Mary's Cemetery. One man who was at that service named Leslie R. Burgum, who was the North Dakota attorney general at the time, actually knew the captain when he was a boy. Another man named Edmond A. Hughes said he was a cabin boy on many of the Missouri River steamboats. A prominent North Dakota historian named Russell Reid also spoke. I've got a great photo of the headstone to show you."

Prez showed them a photo.

"It's beautiful!" said KT.

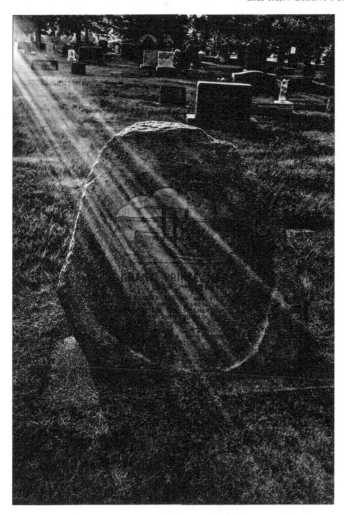

"What does the inscription say?" asked Jessie, with tears in her eyes.

"It reads: *Grant Prince Marsh 1834-1916: A pioneer captain and pilot on Missouri River steamboats. In 1876 he piloted the steamer Far West carrying the wounded from the Little Big Horn to Ft. Lincoln in 54 hours—a feat unparalleled in steamboat history.*

"What an amazing life!" Nick exclaimed.

Chapter 32

What a Sight

It was a remarkable, exciting atmosphere awaiting Sarabiskota in Bismarck and Mandan. There were people from all over the world, and many millions more were watching on their televisions, computers, phones, and other devices. It was hard to believe, but this was even more exciting than Independence Day had been.

It seemed like everyone sensed an exciting climax to the Captain Grant Marsh adventure, and they all wanted to be part of it. Thousands and thousands of people watched from boats on the Missouri River, from the sandbars, and from the riverbanks.

A limited number of aircraft, including the *Flying Teddy*, were allowed to fly over the area. Troy Polymollydoo and Jack Lambert had joined Sarabiskota on board the *Flying Teddy*. Shortly after 1:00 p.m., the first sighting came in. Something was in the sky over Salem Sue, the world's largest cow statue, 23 miles west of Mandan!

Within seconds, the first photo of it appeared on Spacebook, and soon, millions of people had seen it. It was a gigantic 40-foot Captain Grant Marsh, flying west in an upright position toward the Bismarck-Mandan area. Less than ten minutes later, *Flying Teddy* was right behind Captain Marsh.

"It's not a balloon," said Egore. "It's made of some type of lightweight solid material."

"What's propelling it?" asked Jack Lambert.

"It's hard to tell from here," Prez replied. "Whatever it is, it's pretty darn cool."

"Maybe we'll find out tonight at A&B," said Nick.

The Grant Marsh ship flew slowly to Ft. Abraham Lincoln, south of Mandan. Then it began flying north along the Missouri River.

"I hope it lands where I think it's going to land," said Kevin.

"Me too," said Troy. "That would be *so* perfect!"

The next 20 minutes were incredible, as Grant Marsh flew through the air slowly, as people cheered and cheered!

Eventually, Grant Marsh landed feetfirst on the bluff above of the old Northern Pacific Railroad Bridge. A deep voice coming from the gigantic statue said, "This is where I wanted to be buried when I died, but I think enjoying this view will be even better. This is the river I loved so much! It will be my pleasure and joy to keep watch over it *forever*, thinking about all those great, exciting times I had on all those steamboats ... and every night, I will light up the skies around here *spectacularly*. I hope you all enjoyed learning about my life this past week. I don't want to brag, but ... I think now everyone in the world can *see*—that I was the greatest steamboatman in *history*!"

Chapter 33

A & B Surprise

Sarabiskota arrived at Mandan's A&B Pizza at midnight. Egore tried the door. It was unlocked.

They walked in cautiously, Egore leading the way. All the lights suddenly came on. They continued walking, all the way back to the large party room where they liked to eat. When they got there, they got a big surprise—several large tables were pushed together, and they were loaded with hot pizzas and pitchers of pop.

Sitting at the end of one table, facing them, were JB and Madison, smiling.

"You two!?" Doc exclaimed.

"Why!?" asked Prez.

"I'm JB and this is Madison. Please get some pizza and sit down first. We don't want it to get cold."

Everyone got some pizza and pop, but before they started eating, Kari said, "All right, JB and Madison. What's the deal with you two?"

"All right," said JB. "We've been following you guys for several years now, and we've always wanted to work on some projects with you. We wanted to get your attention and maybe impress you too—and the Grant Marsh thing was what we came up with."

"There's no way you did this all by yourselves," said Kevin.

"Oh *no*," said JB. "We've got a lot of help from a few hundred people who work for our company. In fact, it was one of our researchers who found out about Grant Marsh, and she wondered how the greatest steamboatman in history could have been almost forgotten."

"You came up with all this just to get our attention because you want to work with us!?" said Prez, not believing what he was hearing.

"Basically," said JB. "But I have to admit, it was tons of fun, too.

"Well, we're definitely interested," said Kari. "Are you ever going to tell people the whole story?"

"We're used to keeping out of the public eye as much as possible," said Madison.

"Well, this is something you *have* to share," said Prez. "Maybe we can do a long story together for Spacebook, and tell the whole story—maybe even do a book. We can also talk about future projects if you'd like."

"That all sounds good, but right now, I'd like to propose a toast," said Nick.

Everyone raised their glasses.

Nick smiled and said, "May I just say, this past week has been the best **ever!** A toast to you, JB and Madison! And to A&B pizza—and most importantly—to the greatest steamboatman in history—Captain Grant Marsh!"

About the Author

Kevin Kremer got a huge surprise when he began researching the life of Grant Marsh. There were so many exciting and interesting adventures that happened during Captain Marsh's long life. As Kremer was learning more about him, he got a huge bonus—learning about steamboats and the Steamboat Era, things that were mostly new to him.

Kremer grew up in Mandan, North Dakota, and he loves to write books involving that area. He also likes to include his favorite places in Mandan in his writing—including Ohm's Cafe and A&B Pizza.

Dr. Kremer has written, edited, and published more than 100 books, and he loves writing children's books the most. Kremer also likes helping other authors with challenges they are having with their own book projects.

Kremer has a writing-publishing company to help people with book projects of any kind. To contact him regarding book or e-book projects, school author visits, or to purchase books, go to:

Web site: **KevinKremerBooks.com**
E-mail: **snowinsarasota@aol.com**
Facebook: **Kevin Kremer Books**
and **Captain Grant Marsh Book**

KREMER ENJOYING THE WORLD'S BEST HAMBURGERS AT OHM'S
CAFE

NOTHING TOPS SAUERKRAUT AND CANADIAN BACON PIZZA AT
A&B PIZZA

About the Artist

Some of Darrel Aleson's fondest art memories go back to gas station restrooms. It was there, when traveling with his family as a child, that he got his first drawing papers—those brown folded towels. The backseat became Darrel's artist studio as wonderful drawings of trucks, cars, airplanes, and other things appeared on those cheap towels. The rougher the road, the more abstract the drawing. Darrel even won a drawing contest on the "Captain Jim" children's TV show in Fargo.

Finding solace in creating art was a constant for Darrel through childhood, college, medical school, and seminary. People began to view some of his artwork, and they liked it, even asking him to do something for them. Any subject matter was fair game. Word got around and Darrel received many requests over the past 35 years. A self-commissioned piece in 1997 got noticed by *U.S. Art* magazine. Prints of that work have gone to over 40 states and several foreign countries.

Darrel has the same birthday as his identical twin brother, whose accomplished artist daughter did not get her abilities from her dad. Darrel's best accomplishment was to marry his wife, Deborah. She even allowed Darrel the crazy adventure of building and piloting his own aircraft in the early 80s. Darrel and Deborah's daughter, Wendy, and son, Josh, have given them three grandkids to spoil. The Alesons live in beautiful Bismarck. As a retired pastor/hospital chaplain, Darrel is supposed to have more time at his drawing table. He is still waiting for that.

Darrel drawing the *Far West* steamboat

Darrel drawing Captain Grant Marsh

To arrange for a reasonably priced
author visit or to buy other great
books go to:
KevinKremerBooks.com

Published by Kremer Publishing
2019
P.O. Box 1385
Osprey, FL 34229-1385
(941) 822-0549

Made in the USA
Middletown, DE
17 September 2022

73443251R00152